DORSET
in the
AGE *of* STEAM

A HISTORY AND ARCHAEOLOGY OF DORSET INDUSTRY, c.1750–1950

DORSET
—— *in the* ——
AGE *of* STEAM

A HISTORY AND ARCHAEOLOGY OF DORSET INDUSTRY, c.1750–1950

Peter Stanier

DORSET BOOKS

First published in 2002 by Dorset Books
Copyright © 2002 Peter Stanier

ISBN 1 871164 90 7

British Library Cataloguing-in-Publication Data
A CIP data for this book is available from the British Library

DORSET BOOKS
Halsgrove House
Lower Moor Way
Tiverton EX16 6SS
T: 01884 243242
F: 01884 243325
www.halsgrove.com

Printed and bound in Great Britain by Bookcraft, Midsomer Norton

❧ CONTENTS ❧

❧ ACKNOWLEDGEMENTS ❧

It is always satisfying to receive an answer to a query, however small, to be pointed in the right direction or just receive encouragement. I am grateful to all those who have helped with the writing of this book, often when they hardly realised they were. In particular, though, I must thank Mike Bone, John Brown, Colin Burfoot, Richard Clammer, Penny Copland-Griffiths, Peter Crocker, Jo Draper, Peter Lamb, Michael Messenger, Claire Pinder, John Powell, David Reave, Richard Sims, Derrick Warren, Martin Watts and John Willows. My publisher Steven Pugsley has been patient and encouraging throughout.

Staff have been more than helpful at Dorset County Council, Dorset County Reference Library, Dorset County Record Office, Dorset County Museum, Bournemouth & West Hampshire Water Co., Bournemouth Borough Council, Bridport Museum, E.C.C. Ball Clays Ltd, Gillingham Museum, Lyme Regis Town Mill Trust, Museum of Electricity, Poole Museum, Poole Pottery Ltd, Wessex Water's Museum of Water Supply and Weymouth & Portland Museum Service.

For the use of photographs I must thank Maureen Dolamore, Rhrodri Evans, Derrick Warren, Bridport Museum, Dorset County Library, Gillingham Museum, Hall & Woodhouse Ltd, Lyme Regis Town Mill Trust, Poole Pottery Ltd, Verwood & District Potteries Trust, and the Director, British Geological Survey (NERC copyright reserved). All others are from my own collection.

Sacrifices have been made to fit the requirements of this book but hopefully I have hinted where most of these omissions lie somewhere in the text. There is fertile research to be found in many individual areas of industrial archaeology, including those industries hardly touched on here, out in the field and in the archives. Moreover, it is worth pointing out that the Dorset County Council's Historic Buildings and Sites & Monuments Record desperately needs to expand its database of industrial sites. This is just one good reason to get out into the landscape and the archives to record Dorset's industrial heritage.

Peter Stannier, October 2002

☙ PREFACE ❧

Dorsetshire yields Portland stone, Purbeck marble, lime, founders' sand, iron-sand, copperas, alum, pottery clay, pipe clay, fire-bricks, Bovey coal, salt, sheep and cattle, wool, butter, cheese, corn, hay, potatoes and cider ... lime, sea-weed and fish are to be had in most parts for manures, and for meadows the catchwater plan is used. Barley is grown more than wheat; hemp and flax are likewise grown. The dairy is much looked to, and the butter and cheese of Dorsetshire are much esteemed in the London market. The manufactures are sailcloth, sacking, nets and shoe-makers' thread, paper, silk, shirt buttons, agricultural implements, etc, carried on at Bridport, Beaminster, Blandford, Bourton, Gillingham, Sherborne and Wimborne; with malting and brewing. In some of the large towns are iron foundries. Ships and yachts are built at Poole and Bridport. The people on the shore are kept by the fisheries, quarries, and visitors to the watering-places. These latter are Weymouth, Swanage, Lyme Regis and Parkstone.

[KELLY & CO.'S DIRECTORY OF DORSET, 1867]

Standing on the noble viewpoints of Black Down, Bulbarrow or Pilsdon Pen, it is easy to appreciate that Dorset is one of the most attractive counties in England. It is more difficult to believe that the landscape laid out below has harboured any industrial activity. Yet industry did flourish here and in many unlikely corners. Most of these rural industries were directly related to the landscape, its geology and products from the soil. Characteristically, many were small and only locally important but others had a national significance.

What makes Dorset different? Its long industrial history dates back at least to the Iron Age when pottery and Kimmeridge shale bracelets were manufactured and traded beyond the region. The working of shale and Purbeck stone were Roman industries and the Purbeck marble trade was nationally important in the medieval period. The quarries on Portland, surely, have produced the best known and finest building freestone in England, and parts of Dorset will forever remain in London's landmarks, from St Paul's Cathedral to the British Museum, Waterloo Bridge or the Cenotaph. Poole Pottery is a household name but it was the great Staffordshire potteries of Wedgwood and others who first took the high quality ball clay from beneath the Purbeck heaths. Kimmeridge oil shale was less successful and just failed to be used to light the streets of Paris.

Dorset is an agricultural county. Its malted barley was held in great repute in the past and it once produced the 'best and finest beer in England.' Dorset can still boast three traditional working breweries, at Blandford, Bridport and Dorchester. Flax and hemp sustained the justly famous manufacture of nets, ropes and twines at

Bridport where the industry has left a unique legacy. There were silk mills in the north and sailcloth makers in the west. Dorset's foundries made agricultural equipment and steam engines that were exported all over the world.

On the roads, Dorset has two rare tunnels of the early-nineteenth century, the oldest letter-box in England and even gas lighting, while notices still threaten deportation for culprits who injure bridges. Dorset had an early railway in 1806 and a surviving tunnel is one of the oldest in England. The first Argand lamps and true lenses were used at Portland where there are three lighthouse towers. The Portland breakwaters enclose the largest artificial harbour in the United Kingdom. A funnel from Brunel's mighty *Great Eastern* is still in the county. The water and electricity industries have their own industrial museums in Dorset, appropriately housed in a Victorian waterworks and an Edwardian power station. It may be added that some consider that smuggling was once one of Dorset's greatest industries but it has left little or no trace.

This book is mostly concerned with Dorset in the period 1750–1950, which encompasses the rise and decline of the Industrial Revolution and it is one we might term the 'Age of Steam'. Dorset was harboured from the mainstream of the industrial age and there were no heavy industries or satanic mills here, yet the county is surprisingly rich in its industrial archaeology. By highlighting the best sites this book will have achieved its aim if it has revealed a new aspect of Dorset's unique heritage and stimulated the reader to seek out more. The theme throughout is a rural one. It is a personal account of the industrial archaeology that makes up just one thread of Dorset's rich historical past.

It is unhelpful that the county boundary changed more than once during the period of study, with parts being exchanged with neighbouring Devon, Somerset and Hampshire. In the Age of Steam, industrial sites in Bournemouth and Christchurch were in Hampshire, and the reader is reminded that the Dorset of this book is the one of the more familiar post-1974 boundary changes!

This book uses the old weights and measurements (except for some very recent cases) because these were current throughout the period of study. The following conversion table may be helpful:

Length	Weight	
1 inch = 25.4 millimetres	1 pound (lb)	= 0.453 kilogram
1 foot = 0.3 metre	1 hundredweight (cwt)	= 50.8 kilograms
1 yard = 0.91 metre	1 ton	= 1.017 tonne
1 mile = 1.6 kilometres		

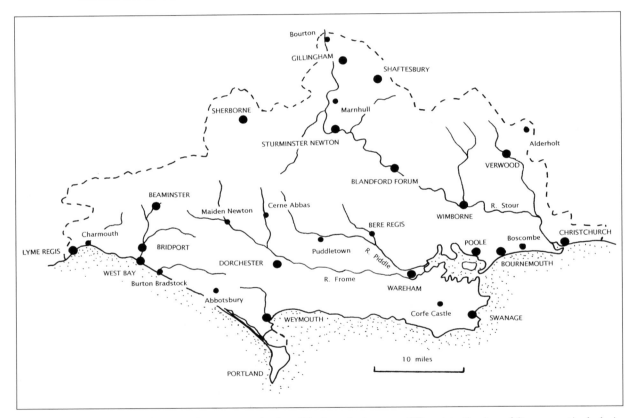

A map of Dorset showing the post-1974 county of today. The boundaries were different in the Age of Steam, particularly in the southeast and the northwest.

1

DORSET'S AGE OF STEAM

Dorset's industrial archaeology is less familiar than its more traditional mainstream archaeology. The countryside has some of the finest archaeological sites in England, where the famous Iron Age hillforts of Maiden Castle, Hod, Hambledon or Eggardon Hill remain powerful monuments in the landscape after 2,000 years. Their massive earthworks were constructed on a civil engineering scale not seen again until the railway navvies carved their way through Dorset in the mid-nineteenth century. The Romans left us the first engineered roads, of which the Ackling Dyke over Cranborne Chase is one of the best in England, and the earthwork of a carefully surveyed aqueduct that still impresses as it contours towards Durnovaria (Dorchester).

Organised quarrying and building industries of the Middle Ages are witnessed in the export of Purbeck marble, and the county's stone churches or the castles at Corfe and Sherborne. Sea trade was evidently well established at places like Lyme Regis and the making of ropes and sails for the Navy began at Bridport during this time. Small industries such as corn mills, potteries, tanneries or salt-works were all of local significance.

The late-sixteenth century saw two unusual industrial processes of note. Copperas or green vitriol (ferrous sulphate) was made from iron pyrites found as nodules or in shales. It was used as a mordant in textile dyeing, tanning and making ink. It also made nitric and sulphuric acids, although there were better sources by the end of the eighteenth century. In 1566 Lord Mountjoy, 'studious in mineral matters', started to make copperas and to boil alum near Canford cliffs or Alum Chine in one of the earliest recorded works in England. Twenty years later the enterprise had passed to the Earl of Huntingdon who found the 'mines' profitable. Although shipments were made from Poole, the distance to London was inconvenient and the works had closed by 1608.

Copperas works on Brownsea Island were reopened by Sir Robert Clayton in the late-seventeenth century. Celia Fiennes visited Brownsea and described in detail how the stones were gathered from the shore, piled in rows and allowed to dissolve in the rain. The residue was collected and boiled in iron pans to extract the copperas which 'lookes cleare like suger-candy.' A building had large pans with great furnaces underneath keeping them boiling. According to John Hutchins, the county historian, Clayton had a copperas works at Studland supplied with stones brought from the Isle of Wight, but it was ruinous by 1700.

Sir William Clavell of Smedmore made alum in the early-seventeenth century from the shales at Kimmeridge. He spent £4000 on the works and a large pier but, alas, his works was forced to close because the rights of alum making in Dorset had been granted elsewhere. The remains of an alum furnace were discovered in 1976 to the east of the quay at Kimmeridge, with evidence that the stream had been diverted as part of these works. Copperas can be produced during alum production, and as late as the mid-1850s there were plans to build an alum plant on Brownsea to make vitriol.

Clavell next ran a glass works in 1617–23 but this too had to be closed. He used oil shale or 'Kimmeridge Coal' as the fuel for the alum and glass works as well as for making salt. The glass works site has been excavated and some traces of salt boiling have been exposed by erosion to the south of the quay at Kimmeridge. The ancient trade of salt making was carried on elsewhere along the coast, most especially around the shores of Poole Harbour.

Within the limitations of his *Tour through the Whole Island of Great Britain*, Daniel Defoe made some reference to industry in Dorset in the 1720s on the eve of the Industrial Revolution. He had most to say about quarrying and shipping. On Purbeck 'vast quarreys of stone' produced paving for houses and streets, with a profitable shipping trade to London. From the Isle of Portland came 'our best and whitest free stone' for St Paul's Cathedral, the Monument and public buildings in London, and it was:

> ... wonderful and well worth the observation of a traveller to see the quarries in the rocks, from whence they are cut out, what stones, and of what prodigious a size are cut out there.

Two lighthouses had been recently erected at Portland. Merchants at the ports of Poole, Weymouth and Lyme Regis all carried on 'considerable' trades with France, Portugal, Spain and Newfoundland. The last was an important fishery, supported most successfully by the men of Poole. Defoe described the 'massy pile' of the Cobb breakwater at Lyme Regis, but there was no harbour at Bridport which was 'a town in which we see nothing remarkable.' He did, however, describe mackerel fishing off the shore at Bridport and declared that Poole's famous oysters were sent to London, Spain, Italy and the West Indies. The finest bonelace in England was made at Blandford, while fine stockings at 'Stourbridge' had once been the best. Defoe was impressed by 600,000 sheep on the downs within a 6-mile radius of Dorchester.

One example of rural Dorset's craft or cottage industries was button making (buttony), which began in Shaftesbury in the 1680s and developed in the surrounding villages until Blandford became the main centre. The buttons were much in demand by high society. Abraham Case's first buttons were 'High Tops', a disc of ram's horn with a hole in the centre and linen cone on top decorated with thread. Case and other agents had depots over north Dorset, and by 1812 around 4000 women and children were said to be involved. The earlier cloth buttons were replaced by ring ones of a special alloy over which designs were threaded, but the industry was killed in the 1840s by Ashton's button machine and the trade moved to Birmingham. Homeworkers provided labour outside the factories for some industries well into the twentieth century, including net braiding and gloving.

The Age of Steam covers the two momentous centuries between 1750 and 1950 which saw the birth, heyday and aftermath of the Industrial Revolution. These times of upheaval changed the character of the nation, although much of Dorset quietly escaped the worst ravages of the revolution. In 1756 the eminent civil engineer John Smeaton came this way while selecting stone for his famous Eddystone Lighthouse and left an account of the quarries at Portland and along the Purbeck sea cliffs. Soon afterwards, in 1765, stone quarries, watermills, windmills, turnpike roads, brick kilns and a limekiln were depicted on Isaac Taylor's first informative Dorset map of 1765. John Claridge and William Stevenson described the state of some Dorset industries when writing of the agriculture in the county in 1793 and 1815. It was not until the second half of the nineteenth century that any significant change was seen to have taken hold in the countryside. This was just the period about which Thomas Hardy wrote, when the old country ways were giving way to 'progress', including steam. His books include references to corn milling (*The Trumpet Major*), quarrying on Portland (*The Well-Beloved*), steam threshing (*Tess of the d'Urbervilles*), railway trains and a paddle-steamer voyage between Weymouth and Lulworth Cove (*Desperate Remedies*), all scenes which the author based on his own observations.

Although much of rural Dorset remained an industrial backwater, its products did reach the world outside. Nets and ropes were renowned far beyond Bridport, and Portland's freestone and Purbeck's paving stones helped build the monuments of the Industrial Revolution beyond the county, in docks, dockyards, bridges, public buildings, memorials and roads. From Swanage came John Mowlem and his nephew George Burt, who paved the streets of London with their stone, and established a major civil engineering firm that still bears the name of Mowlem.

John Mowlem's granite tomb at Swanage. Mowlem (1788–1868) and his nephew George Burt founded a major contracting firm and adorned the town with curious stones and artefacts brought back from demolished London buildings.

Many of Dorset's traditional industries were intimately linked with the natural resources provided by the landscape, geology and soils. The county had a long reliance on water power, and its many streams and rivers turned the wheels of corn mills for centuries. A wide number of other applications by the nineteenth century included flax processing, paper making, sawmilling, snuff making, textiles, breweries, water pumping and eventually electricity generation. The significance of water power cannot be underestimated, even on the smallest streams. For example, in 1823 there were two corn mills, three cloth manufacturing mills, a fulling mill and an oil mill along the final mile of the River Lim at Lyme Regis. In

Water was an important source of power in Dorset throughout the Age of Steam. This is the wheel at Maiden Newton Mill.

east Dorset, at least nine water-powered sites included corn mills, a bone mill, paper mill and sawmill in 12 miles of the River Allen between Wimborne St Giles and Wimborne. As long as water was reliable and the industry small, there was a reluctance to invest and water power held out far longer than otherwise against steam machinery. The installation of turbines in the later-nineteenth century gave new life to water power, and even wind power made a small contribution to milling and water pumping in the Age of Steam.

Steam power for industry made a slow start in Dorset. The greatest restriction on full industrial

Bourton foundry and old flax mill in about 1900. This picture, showing the 60-feet diameter waterwheel and smoking chimneys, captures the essence of industry in the rural Dorset landscape.

GILLINGHAM MUSEUM

development was the lack of coal which, before the railways, came either by sea into the ports or into the north of the county by costly land carriage from the Somerset coalfield. As seen above, Kimmeridge shale was used occasionally as a fuel but not to raise steam. After slow beginnings, early references to steam engines in Dorset began to appear in the 1830s. A 'beautiful' steam engine was destroyed in a fire at a linseed oil mill at Lyme Regis in January 1832 and a new steam engine of 'considerable power' was reported at a soda water manufactory at Dorchester in 1836. Factory Returns of 1838 recorded three larger steam engines in the flax mills around Bridport and Burton Bradstock in west Dorset, where they supplemented the power of eight waterwheels. At the same date wages were paid to 'Leeds men' who were installing machinery at the new Priory Mill, Bridport. This was the first purpose-designed steam-powered spinning mill in the town and the surviving building has clear evidence of where its beam engine once stood.

Dorset was far behind its neighbours in matters of steam. Wiltshire's first engine had been installed in a cloth mill at Trowbridge in 1805 and there were 39 steam-powered textile mills by the 1830s. Two Boulton & Watt beam engines began work in 1809–12 at the famous Crofton pumping station on the Kennet & Avon Canal, while in Somerset a Boulton & Watt engine worked briefly at a Quantocks copper mine from 1817–21.

Railways are perhaps mostly associated with steam and Dorset was only six years behind those two counties, which gained their first locomotives in 1841. Yet railways were not new to Dorset, for a horse-drawn tramway had first carried clay across the Purbeck heaths back in 1806, which was remarkably early for a county perceived as being far from the centre of industrial progress. Steam locomotion arrived with the opening of the Southampton & Dorchester Railway in 1847. This was during Britain's great period of 'railway mania' and within two decades Dorset had an established network of mainline routes and branches, all operated by steam. The eminent engineer Isambard Kingdom Brunel planned the broad-gauge railway line from Yeovil to Dorchester and Weymouth. The railways revolutionised the movement of passengers and goods in the county. They carried away stone, clay, beer and agricultural produce, and they brought in coal and did much to encourage a growing tourist industry.

The Age of Steam: this horizontal engine manufactured by Gimsons of Leicester once worked in the Blandford Brewery of Hall & Woodhouse, where it is now preserved.

HALL & WOODHOUSE

Meanwhile at sea, a steam packet service had run from Weymouth since 1827 and the first locally-owned steamship, the *Rose*, ran from Weymouth to Southampton in 1840–47, connecting with the railway there until the line was extended to Dorchester. In 1848 Joseph Cosens brought the *Highland Maid* into service between Weymouth and Portland, thus beginning a long history of running excursion steamers for nearly 120 years. Brunel's *Great Eastern* caused some local excitement when she put into Portland Harbour in 1859 after a mid-Channel accident. The giant steamship left, minus a funnel section which still remains in the county at the Sutton Poyntz waterworks.

The second half of the century saw the building of Portland Breakwater, one of the great civil engineering monuments of the Victorian period. James Meadows Rendel and Sir John Coode were closely involved and the latter lent his hand to other works in Dorset, including repairs to the west pier at Bridport and designing a new bridge for Portland. This was at a time of increasing activity in Portland's quarries and military defensive projects.

Stationary steam engines increased in number after the mid-nineteenth century. Usually small, they were applied to a variety of industries, such as textile and flax mills, breweries, brickworks, gasworks, sawmills and agriculture. Large

steam-powered stone sawmills were set up on Portland from the 1870s, at about which time steam cranes were introduced into the quarries there. Larger steam engines became increasingly important at water pumping stations. Traction engines for heavy haulage and ploughing appeared and in 1868 Francis Eddison established a large works and depot at Dorchester, followed later by steamrollers. Vertical and horizontal steam engines, locomotives and road vehicles for home use or export were made in Dorset at foundries and engineering works, notably by E.S. Hindley at Bourton and Stephen Lewin at Poole.

By the turn of the century Bridport and Poole were the most truly industrialised towns, their industries dominated at the former by net and twine making, and at the latter by potteries, pipes and bricks. The growing conurbation around Poole, Bournemouth and Christchurch was in marked contrast to the generally rural picture elsewhere. While obsolete practices continued in Dorset's long-established industries, large outside organisations brought in new types of industries, such as the torpedo works at Wyke Regis in 1891 and the cordite factory complex at Holton Heath in 1916; significantly, both were involved with defence.

During the first half of the twentieth century gas, oil and diesel engines commonly took over from steam at smaller industrial works and, finally, electric power proved more versatile to operate. By 1950 steam was mostly in evidence on the railways but engines were at work elsewhere. For example, steam power was generating electricity at Herrison Hospital in 1950 and steam engines carried on their work at the Sutton Poyntz and Walford Bridge water pumping stations until 1958–59. A steam chain ferry at Sandbanks ran until 1959. Steam lingered on into the 1960s. Cosens & Co.'s last Weymouth paddle-steamer, the *Embassy*, made her final excursion in September 1966 and was towed away to Dutch shipbreakers in the following May. The last steam train on a regular service ran in July 1967

on the Southern Region's Weymouth to Waterloo line. Poole industrial archaeologists recorded a Wren & Hopkinson horizontal cross-compound engine of c.1870 still working at J.T. Sydenham & Co.'s sawmill at Hamworthy in 1968. It had been installed second-hand seventy-eight years previously, but its days were numbered. It was dismantled two years later and remains in the Poole Museum's store.

After the interruptions of two world wars in the twentieth century, the Dorset of 1950 was still emerging from the Age of Steam. The 1950s and 60s saw the last of many traditional industrial

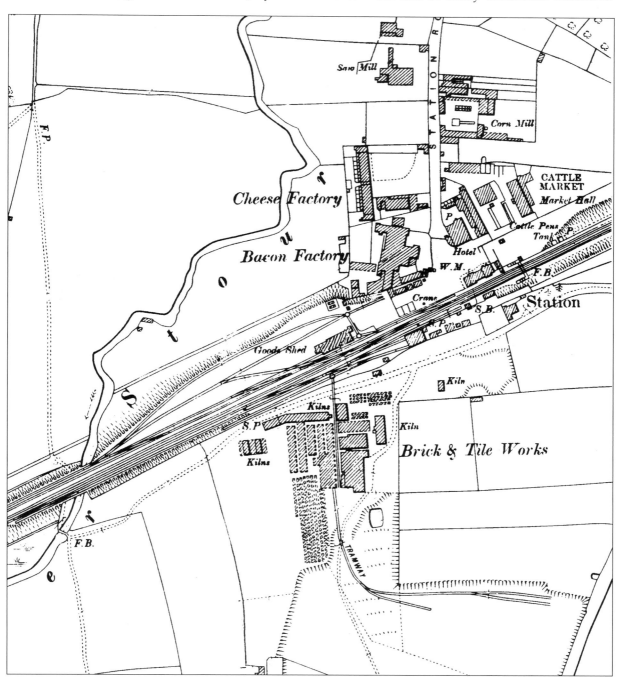

Gillingham industries in 1900, from the Ordnance Survey 25-inch map. This typifies the small rural town with a railway station, with nearby industrial activity including the brickworks, bacon and cheese factories, corn mill, sawmill and market.

practices, and progress in the ensuing years was to change some places beyond recognition. Older industries vanished, as did the building styles that so often betrayed their function, and we now live in a world of industrial estates, with new industries operating in buildings designed like warehouses. Housing developments have overrun past industrial sites and changed the face of towns such as Poole, where very little survives of its industries of less than a century ago.

Before the coming of the railways public transport on the roads was at a leisurely pace in the early-nineteenth century, when daily coaches and carriers were notified in directories or newspapers. The twentieth century saw a revolution in road transport, with the development of motor cars, lorries and buses. Even trams and trolleybuses made an appearance around Bournemouth. At the beginning of the century traction engines were commonplace. By 1950, steamrollers were still common and other road traffic was comparatively light. The railways, still worked by steam, had yet to undergo the pruning of the 1960s. Half a century later the transport industry bears little resemblance. Just try comparing Dorset's main roads and bypasses, the railways, cargo and passenger shipping, or even air travel.

A Burrel traction engine with two trailers loaded with large stone blocks in Easton Lane, Portland, April 1930. This picture indicates the power of traction engines but road surfaces paid a terrible price. In the following year Bath and Portland Stone Firms Ltd replaced their engines with a fleet of Sentinel steam lorries.

BRITISH GEOLOGICAL SURVEY

There were changes too in the world of communications. The archaeology of communications ranges from the Admiralty signal and telegraph stations of the early-nineteenth century (there are traces of one at Round Down above Anvil Point, near Swanage), to the development of the electric telegraph from about 1840 and the first telephones later in the century. Radio developments saw the building of a Marconi radio station on the Bridport road outside Dorchester in 1927, transmitting to the Americas and the Far East. After closure fifty years later, the buildings became a printing works.

Electricity was the power of the twentieth century, tentatively generated at first by small water turbines or diesel sets. By 1950 there was Poole Power Station, and within a few years construction began on the first experimental nuclear generators at Winfrith Heath at a time when some industries were still using steam engines.

Industrial archaeology grew rapidly as a discipline from the 1960s onwards, stimulated by an awareness of all that was being lost in this new world of post-war developments across the whole country. The subject is concerned, most especially, with the recording of industrial remains that tell of technological, social and economic developments in the period following the mid-eighteenth century. The setting of industrial activity in rural or urban landscapes is of particular importance in Dorset. Most early literature on the subject included Dorset only in passing. Kenneth Hudson's pioneering *Industrial Archaeology of Southern England* (1968) gave an account of industrial activity across five counties, with brief entries on Dorset including quarrying, ports and shipping, and the manufacture of bricks, paper, pottery, gloves, buttons, lace, silk, sailcloth, ropes and nets. This book is given added interest when it is realised that many of the industries and their premises have since passed into history. Keith Falconer's wider *Guide to England's Industrial Heritage* (1980) listed 23 sites in Dorset, including breweries, mills, tramways, ports and kilns. The first small gazetteer for Dorset was written by this author in 1989 to present an overview of industrial archaeology in the county. It included around 150 sites, and the subsequent disappearance of several only reinforces the value of recording the industrial archaeology before it is lost. Other authors have covered particular Dorset industries, and individual studies include publications by Donald Young on brickyards and Mike Bone on rope and net making at Bridport. There have been other surveys of quarries, limekilns, mills, milestones and toll-houses, but much remains to be done.

Industrial archaeology is also concerned with preservation wherever desirable or feasible. Keeping to the theme of steam machinery, five stationary engines are preserved in Dorset breweries: two at Blandford, two more at the old Weymouth Brewery, with a fifth engine at the Palmers' brewery in Bridport. And steam is not

Portable steam engines were towed by contractors to farms for driving threshing machines or other equipment. This example, made by Marshalls of Gainsborough, is seen here at Shaftesbury.

The march of time: the jibs of modern cranes and high banks of spoil dominate the scene as stone quarries are carved from the open fields at Silklake, Portland, in 1930.

BRITISH GEOLOGICAL SURVEY (NERC COPYRIGHT RESERVED)

dead in Dorset. At the start of the twenty-first century steam is working on the restored Swanage Railway, and occasional steam-hauled excursion trains pass through Dorset at Gillingham and Sherborne on the line between Salisbury and Yeovil Junction. The popular Great Dorset Steam Fair is now a major annual event when the county hosts Europe's largest steam fair with hundreds of working traction engines, roadrollers, fairground and other steam machinery congregating on acres of downland fields near Pimperne. Even on the water, the world's last sea-going paddle-steamer *Waverley* has been cruising in and out of Weymouth and Poole since 1978.

This book covers the historical development and archaeology of Dorset's main industries in the landscape, tracing them from agriculture to extractive, processing, manufacturing and transport, to utilities, housing and military works. Bridport, Weymouth, Portland and Purbeck have notable concentrations of industrial archaeology, although much has been lost at Poole. Ironically, for all its beauty, Purbeck has perhaps the longest history of industrial activity in Dorset, with quarries and mines for limestone, chalk, sand, brick clay, ball clay, shale and oil. Even the farming district of the Blackmoor Vale in rural north Dorset had quarries, limekilns, mills, brickworks, breweries, turnpike roads and a railway.

The extractive industries include open quarries or pits for stone, gravel, sand, clay and ironstone, and their archaeology is one of numerous overgrown workings or stone faces with evidence of stone-cutting, cranes and tramways. In addition, there were the mines for stone, ball clay and oil shale, mostly confined to the Isle of Purbeck. There was no coal to mine for fuel, despite attempts to find it, and the intermittent shale workings at Kimmeridge were never very suc-

cessful. Only at the very end of the period was petroleum oil discovered and exploited to eventually grow into a major industry and export from the county.

Processing industries directly related to mineral extraction include stone dressing, lime burning, cement making, bricks, tiles and the pottery industries. Despite the significance of all these in the past, demolitions have ensured that only the remote limekilns survive in any great number to witness a locally important industry.

The last traditional type of limekilns in the south of England continued burning at Shillingstone until the very end of the twentieth century. Two pairs of kilns are in the foreground and the hydration plant is behind.

Agriculture was a major provider of raw materials for other industries such as brewing, malting, milling, paper making, textiles, and rope, twine and net making. Dorset-grown barley and hemp were both noted for the highest quality, while animal products went to tanning, gloving and the food processing and dairy industries. There are many corn mills throughout Dorset, some on very ancient sites, but the most distinctive industrial buildings are the later Victorian breweries and malt-houses. Some mills for textiles and net making are also of note. Engineering works and foundries relied on outside materials, particularly iron and bronze, but made a whole range of products for local agriculture or for export. All these industries relied on sources of power, from animal, water and wind, to steam, gas, diesel and electricity.

The efficient movement of raw materials and finished products ensured the success of many industries and all forms of transport have left behind a legacy of toll-houses, milestones, bridges, tunnels, stations, ports and shipping facilities. Unlike its neighbours, Dorset never had a canal, although one route was planned. Early air transport had a limited impact on Dorset, and this was mostly in the military field.

Service industries or public utilities were established in the nineteenth century, first with gas in the 1830s, followed by water in the 1850s and early electricity generation by the end of the century. Most of these three utilities, once in the hands of private companies, local boards or councils, were nationalised after the Second World War. Many of the old town gasworks were swept away after the introduction of natural gas, but water pumping stations and reservoir towers remain, along with some early examples of electricity power stations. Sewage schemes, not discussed here further, were an essential part of the water industry since the later-nineteenth century.

As a period subject, industrial archaeology includes the evidence for all human activities and this must include housing for industrial workers or establishments catering for the religious or secular needs of the population, as varied as places of worship, workhouses, prisons, cinemas and seaside resorts. Space only permits the briefest mention.

No archaeological study of our period is complete without reference to the military engineering projects undertaken on an industrial scale, particularly from about 1850. Military works range from the massive coastal defences and forts around Portland and Weymouth, the Portland Breakwater, explosives manufacturing at Holton Heath, to airfields or pillboxes of the Second World War. Wartime brought developments: for example Worth Matravers played a significant role in the development of radar, and the Bailey Bridge was invented at Christchurch. In recent years the Defence of Britain Project has been surveying the archaeology of both world wars. We begin, though, with the oldest industry of all: agriculture.

2

FARMING IN THE INDUSTRIAL AGE

Agriculture has shaped the Dorset scenery we know today, but its story in our period is one of prosperity alternating with years of depression. The state of Dorset agriculture was described around the time of the Napoleonic Wars by John Claridge (1793) and William Stevenson (1815). High prices and good times for farmers were cut short as soon as war ended, and poor harvests and low agricultural wages culminated in riots in 1830 and the transportation of the Tolpuddle Martyrs in 1834. A period of recovery in Victorian times saw landowners experimenting with crops and animal breeds and applying steam power on purpose-built model farms. In the 1870s steam ploughing broke up large areas of chalk downland for the first time, but at the end of the decade increasing imports of foreign wheat and meat products brought the great agricultural depression, during which many farmers left the land. Meanwhile, railways had opened up distant markets for milk and dairy products in London and elsewhere. There was a brief recovery in the First World War, before depression returned in the 1920s. The twentieth century saw enormous changes in agriculture when tractors slowly replaced horses, although not completely until after the Second World War. Steam threshing continued in places until the 1950s after which the combine harvester took over.

To this writer, it is the unusual and curious that makes agriculture a part of industrial archaeology. On farms or large estates this embraces water meadow systems, field drains, special barns, model farms, sheepwashes, churn-stands, hydraulic rams, horse mills, watermills, steam power, dovecotes, ice houses, and a great deal more. This broad subject also includes portable engines, traction engines, tractors and a catalogue of implements such as ploughs, rakes, harrows, rollers, threshing machines or chaff-cutters, many manufactured by local foundries. Limekilns were also part of the farming scene, while quarries and brickyards supplied materials for agricultural buildings. Malting, brewing, tanning, gloving, textiles and the flax and hemp industries were directly related to agriculture, while new food industries such as dairies (milk, cheese and butter) or bacon factories, took full advantage of the railway age for distributing their products.

Power on the farm came from oxen, horses, water and steam in the nineteenth century. Stevenson devoted a considerable section to 'thrashing mills' most of which had been erected in the early years of the century and were powered by one to six horses (one had six oxen). An incentive was the scarcity of labour brought about by the wars, and at Bere Regis a Mr Garland found his machine 'useful because it can be managed mostly by women.' Stevenson named at least 28 machines around the county, describing many of them in detail. For example:

> Mr Billet's thrashing-mill, at Warmwell, is a two horse power, made by Mr Maggs. The velocity is increased about 70 times, by two large wheels, and two ones in the common way; the drum is closed, and has eight beaters, and the apron, in this machine, and nearly all others in this county, is of cast iron, with a kind of square teeth pointing downwards towards the drum. As the straw passes between the drum and the apron, and as the corn is in some measure rubbed out by friction against the apron, the teeth should be small and numerous, something like saw-teeth, and leaning the same way as the straw passes. In this respect the thrashing-mills of this county are not so well constructed as in some other places.

> The iron segments of which Mr Billet's horse-wheel was composed, were made too slightly, and broke in consequence. They are now made more substantially, and the teeth are longer and more rounded towards the points; and in Mr Billet's opinion, the machine works more freely on that account. The horses work the machine by a whipple-tree, or swingle-tree, which is hooked near the end of the shaft; though, by the original plan, the harness was attached to pieces of timber descending on each side of their shoulders.

Two man-powered machines had been set aside in favour of horses and a third had been converted to horse power. There were four powered by water, and another at Tarrant Crawford could be worked by horse or water. Mr Goodenough's water-powered machine at Frampton (formerly six horses) cost £400 and had worked for seven years with 'very trivial repairs.' This was one of four machines of six horse power supplied to Dorset farmers by Mr Geekie of Scotland. The straw was fed over an open drum with six beaters and 20 to 23 sacks of wheat were thrashed in a ten-hour day with the help of five women and two men. Not all were a success: a four-horse machine at Pokeswell had 'answered very ill', and a water-powered one at Frane Farm, near

Dorchester, did not thrash to the farmer's satisfaction, perhaps because this was the only recorded machine in Dorset where the straw passed under and not over the drum. Water power was a poor choice for a machine at Bexington which had no water for three or four months.

Roundhouses were built to contain horse wheels and Stevenson mentions one at Monckton, near St Giles, where the cost of this four-horse threshing machine was 120 guineas, beside the roundhouse. Horse-mill houses were usually built onto the

Thatched horse-mill house at West Farm, Winterborne Whitechurch. Inside, horses walked in a circle to turn a horse engine which transferred power by a layshaft to agricultural equipment in an adjacent barn (since demolished).

Woodwork in the roof structure of the Winterborne Whitechurch horse-mill house.

side of the barn in which the work took place, but a rare survival at Winterborne Whitechurch now stands alone. This brick roundhouse with a thatched roof at West Farm *(SY 840997)* may date from the eighteenth century. It measures 34 feet in diameter internally but contains no gear except for a layshaft bearing. Other horse mills are known to have worked malt-grinding rollers at Higher Melcombe, and pumping gear at Chalmington Home Farm, near Cattistock, and Bloxworth House, near Bere Regis.

Wherever possible, farms and estates utilised streams to work machinery for milling and preparing animal feeds, for sawing, water pumping and even milking. The waterwheel, though, tied the activity to one spot on the farm. Most wheels had a ring-drive bolted onto the outside, engaging with a small pinion attached to a layshaft running to the machinery in a building. These wheels were lightly constructed while the gearing arrangement increased the take-off speed.

Except on the largest farms, most wheels were only needed for a few hours a day and so could be sited close to a spring which refilled a small pond overnight. With chalk streams there is usually a good flow. Roke Farm *(SY 835960)*, near Bere Regis, has a low breastshot wheel, 15-feet diameter by 4-feet wide, alongside a brick building of 1890 containing animal feed crushers. Disused since 1947, the wheel underwent restoration in 1983–85. Blashenwell Farm *(SY 951803)*, near Kingston, has a waterwheel at a barn just yards from a spring and pond. Its 16-feet-diameter iron breastshot wheel, by Munden & Armfield of Ringwood, has been idle since 1943.

Longer shafts transferred power some distance from the wheel. Forston Farm *(SY 666955)*, near Godmanstone, has a low breastshot iron wheel, 16-feet diameter by 5-feet 5-inches wide, from which a shaft ran to a barn for working a pump,

This 16-feet diameter waterwheel at Forston Farm in the Cerne Valley drove machinery in a barn via a ring drive and layshaft.

saw, millstones, crusher and, lastly, a milking machine. Water came from a weir on the River Cerne along a brick-built leat but increasing water shortages led to a diesel engine being installed at the barn. A pitchback wheel of 20-feet diameter by 4-feet wide at Hewish Farm, south of Milton Abbas *(ST 806002)*, drove a pump and threshing machine in a barn via a pinion and 175-feet underground shaft. When this machinery became obsolete the wheel generated electricity. At Trigon Farm *(SY 884886)*, near Wareham, a shaft of 300 feet passed through a tunnel from a high breastshot wheel (14 feet by 6 feet) on the River Piddle. Thus a generator (c.1901), circular saw bench and pump could be run at the farm buildings where a governor controlled the hatch, and therefore the speed of the wheel, via a second shaft. This wheel says much for the late-Victorian engineers, for it was installed in 1886 by which time steam power was widely available for farm work.

Ring drive, pinion and layshaft at Trigon Farm. The water-wheel was made by Hossey of Dorchester, and the ring drive by Lott & Walne.

The largest farm wheel in Dorset is an iron over-shot wheel, 26-feet diameter by 2-feet 2-inches wide, hidden below floor level inside a building at Toller Fratrum Farm *(SY 578973)*. It came from Sprake of Bridport in 1832 and drove millstones to prepare animal feeds, a chaff-cutter and other machinery including sheep shearers before it stopped in the 1940s. The farm is not on a stream and water was brought to the millpond by a long leat, since filled in, which crossed a lane by an iron aqueduct on pillars. Another internal wheel drove a pair of millstones, and chaff and turnip cutters, inside Old Barn, Stalbridge Park *(ST 725176)*. Measuring 13 feet 10 inches by 3 feet 2 inches, this iron wheel was made by Maggs & Hindley of Bourton in 1862. It was possible to store enough water from the stream for just 1½ hours of work.

High farming of the mid-nineteenth century included the application of steam power. By 1854, Louis Ruegg was able to note 13 steam engines on Dorset farms as a feature of farm improvement, in addition to three or four portable steam threshing machines. The Rev. Anthony Huxtable had two farms at Sutton Waldron to which he applied all scientific arts of cultivation and also had two steam engines. His hill farm of 250 acres on the chalk had a chimney and an 'extensive range of buildings' standing in contrast to their surroundings in a desolate district:

> *The engine of 6-horsepower, besides driving a combined threshing, straw-shaking, winnowing and sacking machine, cuts by one of Cornes' implements most of the straw into chaff, whilst the rest of the straw is propelled into a large, dry, covered shed close to the cattle stalls. The same engine also is used for working two pairs of millstones, a flour dressing machine, a large bone mill, and a bean bruiser; and after work at night the remaining steam cooks the roots for the pigs. Above the boiler and engine is a large drying-room where the surplus heat hardens the corn for grinding, and in wet weather is found of great service.*

Ruegg also described methods of keeping and feeding cattle and sheep. The west farm, mainly in clay, was under the same management, 'the chief peculiarity of the system being the arrangement for conveying liquid manure in underground clay-pipes for distribution at various parts of the farm.'

Henry Charles Sturt's home farm at Crichell had a steam engine performing similar functions to Huxtable's, as well as pumping water to the house, stables and farmyard, and sawing all the timber for estate buildings. Sturt's tenants were said to be the first to buy their own fixed steam engines, including one erected at Rushton Farm by Mr Ford, 'whose fat Hereford cattle occupy conspicuous places in the prize lists at Christmas.' James Farquharson at Langton, Blandford, had a threshing machine powered by steam, using coal shipped from Scotland, as Newcastle coals were said to have burnt out the furnace bars (the fact that his 4500 acres were 'managed by intelligent Scotch bailiffs' may be just coincidence).

Nearby, the steam engine at Lord Portman's Bryanston Farm was said to be the most efficient in the county, driving a sawmill, bone mill, chaff-cutters, corn and cake crushers, malt mill and a threshing machine. Waste steam was used in an apparatus to steam animal food. Thirty years later, in 1883, a turbine was installed by Messrs Gilkes of Kendal, rated at 10bhp operating on a

Buildings at Bryanston Home Farm dating from the period of Victorian high farming. There was accommodation for single farm workers and the base of a chimney for a steam engine is seen in the background. A water turbine was later installed here.

head of 100 feet at a speed of 960rpm. The head of water came from a reservoir to which water was pumped up by a waterwheel from the River Stour. Ruegg observed that the 'most spirited landowners' had spent heavily on farm buildings. Indeed, some notable barns and other buildings were erected on model farms in this period and also in the early-twentieth century.

Acres of abandoned water meadow systems make a distinct landscape along the Frome and Piddle valleys and their chalk tributaries, although not quite unique to the county. The first true water meadows in England appear to have been developed at Affpuddle by 1610 and thereafter agriculturalists came to Dorset to learn their management. The leading expert George Boswell of Puddletown wrote a treatise on the subject in 1779, with plans and a drawing of hatch arrangements, and by 1793 Claridge estimated 50,000 acres were under water meadows.

Floated water meadows were closely tied to corn growing and sheep husbandry. In late winter and early spring, water was diverted from the river via the main carrier, controlled by a series of hatches (sluices) and distributed by carriers to flow across the meadow and return to the river by drains. All was carefully engineered to maintain a thin sheet of water flowing continuously over the meadows to provide insulation against frost and deposit fine sediment. This enriched the soil and encouraged an early growth of grass for graz-

ing by sheep in the early spring when the chalk downs were bare. Thus larger downland flocks could be overwintered, and when they were herded onto arable land between harvest and sowing, their dung fertilised the ground and increased the yield of corn. After this 'early bite' the meadows were again flooded to bring on further growth for an abundant summer harvest of hay. Dairy cows grazed the meadows in the autumn and then the ditches were cleared, the hatches repaired and the cycle was repeated. The system began to decline in the depressions of the late-nineteenth century when corn production fell and artificial fertilisers were used.

There is evidence for water meadows along the Frome Valley between Dorchester and Wool, and upstream beyond Maiden Newton, including the side valleys of the Cerne, Sydling Water and Hooke. There is also the Piddle from around Puddletown towards Wareham, and its tributary the Devil's Brook, with more on other chalk streams. Stevenson mentioned water meadows 'only capable of occasional watering' near the Cashmore turnpike, which must have been high up on the stream at Gussage St Michael. The Stour was prone to flooding and water meadows were never really part of farming in the Blackmoor Vale basin, although some were tried. For example, there are traces of water meadows in the steep valley of the Stirchel, a tributary of the Stour at Melbury Abbas. The patterns of abandoned channels for carriers and drains are more clearly visible

Water meadows in the Frome Valley, near Cokers Frome, just north of Dorchester, from the 25-inch Ordnance Survey map. Sluices, carriers, drains and an aqueduct are clearly marked.

from the air, and the surviving sluices and hatch mechanisms made by local founders are worthy of further study. The management of water meadows sometimes came into conflict with the use of waterwheels, and complex tailraces at Forston and Trigon were cut to pass away under the carrier stream. A later aspect of some clear chalk streams was the laying out of watercress beds. These were more localised features, such as around Bere Regis, Empool, Cranborne and Spetisbury.

Three iron hatches stand in abandoned water meadows near Puddletown. They were made by Galpin of Dorchester and are survivors of a once extensive system of water management in the chalk valleys.

RHODRI EVANS

With so many sheep in Dorset, annual shearing was a big event, but first their fleeces had to be washed. Traditionally, women stood in a stream and held each sheep under the water, but by 1800 sheepwashes had been built at Abbotsbury, Frampton and many other places. A sheepwash was constructed in a stream, with masonry walls narrowing at the lower end where boards were inserted in slots to form an artificial pool into which the sheep were pushed and immersed by men holding crooks and poles. Sometimes a slope at the edge helped the bedraggled sheep escape afterwards. Sheepwashes were far more efficient and less disagreeable than the old method. They were once common, particularly in the chalk areas, and a good number marked on the old Ordnance Survey maps still survive. As an example, a sheepwash at Ibberton *(ST 786079)*, below the chalk escarpment of Bulbarrow, was used from at least 1785 until 1968, and was restored by the parish council in 1998. Another excellent survival is visible from the bridleway along the old Roman road near Gussage All Saints *(ST 994110)*. It is brick lined, oval shaped and it has iron grooves to hold the hatch boards.

A well-preserved sheepwash in the stream at Gussage All Saints, typical of many built throughout Dorset in the nineteenth century.

Hydraulic rams supplied water to large houses and farms from the early-nineteenth century onwards. These simple pumps used the volume and fall of a stream to raise a much lesser quantity of water to where it was required. Although the apparent wastage of water was great, hydraulic rams proved reliable and efficient until most fell out of use with the introduction of mains water. Many rams were at remote sites and for this reason they may survive today. Like sheepwashes, the rams and ram houses have hardly been studied by the industrial archaeologist. In the later-nineteenth and early-twentieth centuries small wind engines were occasionally erected on farms to pump water.

Of ephemeral interest, but fast vanishing, are the twentieth-century roadside churn-stands at farm entrances where milk churns were left for collection by the dairy company's lorries. They became redundant with the introduction of bulk milk tanker collections at the farm itself since the 1960s. 'Agriculture' may sit uneasily with 'industry' but there is still a large field of potential research here for the industrial archaeologist.

Octagonal granary on staddle stones at Wyke Farm near Gillingham. This form is said to have been valued by agricultural improvers and Methodists.

Farming and corn milling: cultivating a Portland field with the recently abandoned north windmill in the background, in about 1900.

WEYMOUTH & PORTLAND MUSEUM SERVICE

3

❧ DORSET STONE ❦

Dorset's greatest industry is stone quarrying, and the names of Portland and Purbeck are famed throughout Britain. Other limestones have been used for buildings in west and north Dorset, while sandstone was quarried in the north and parts of the southeast; everywhere, the chalk has been quarried for lime burning and even building. Quarrying for roadstone and aggregates became an important twentieth-century industry.

The Romans quarried stone, and there is ample evidence from their buildings, but the great age of quarrying began with the building of churches and castles by the Normans. Carved and polished Purbeck marble was the most famous stone of the medieval period, and Portland also exported its fine white freestone. The greatest developments in quarrying took place from the eighteenth to the twentieth centuries; stone was especially important to the Victorian builders. The quarrymen took advantage of natural joints and bedding planes and extracted stone blocks by hammering wedges into a line of pits. The marks of wedge-pits can be found showing tool marks on some quarry faces on Portland and Purbeck. This ancient method was replaced in the twentieth century by plugs and feathers inserted into holes made by compressed air drills.

Quarrymen splitting a block of Portland stone at St Paul's Quarry in 1930, using scales and wedges. A shallow groove was first 'pitted' with a 'twabill' (lying on the stone on the left). Quarrymen's marks are part of the archaeology of quarries.

BRITISH GEOLOGICAL SURVEY

Portland and Purbeck have dominated the industry in Dorset and both have some of the most rewarding quarry archaeology in the South of England. The Portland stone industry has left a landscape of open quarries and back-filled ground. The quarrymen removed a thick overburden of marls, shales, limestones and hard Cap rock to gain the valuable Portland stone beds of the tough shelly Roach, the prized white freestone of the Whitbed, and the base bed. The Cherty Series below were of no value except for roadstone. Huge quantities of waste were either tipped over the cliffs or back-filled behind walls of large stone blocks in the quarries. Disused quarries therefore have acres of this waste separated from the final working face by just a narrow gully.

Stone was first exploited among the landslips and cliffs of the northeast side of Portland. Quarrying as an industry really began in the early-seventeenth century, when stone was shipped from a new pier to London for Inigo Jones's Banqueting House. London was always the main market, especially after the Great Fire of 1666 when Sir Christopher Wren chose Portland stone for St Paul's Cathedral and other buildings. Stones of up to 8 tons were shipped from 1676 to 1708, and over 50,000 tons eventually went for the cathedral. Wren controlled the 'King's Quarries' along the East Cliff and provided shipping jetties. Down below the high cliffs, the East Weare, Penn's Weare and Southwell Landslip have huge masses of slipped and tilted stone, with squared blocks and piles of quarry waste throughout. In the early days stone was hauled down to be shipped from New, King's, Folly and Durdle Piers, with others at Church Ope Cove, Chene and Freshwater Bay. Only Durdle Pier survives, with an old timber crane for launching small fishing boats. The exposed west coast also has evidence of stone working, in West Weare and south of Mutton Cove.

Quarrying on Portland was well established in 1756 when John Smeaton was seeking stone for his Eddystone Lighthouse. He described how the Cap was blasted off with gunpowder and then wedges were used to cut up the 'merchantable beds' beneath, before:

> … the quarryman with a tool called a kevel, by a repetition of sturdy blows soon reduces a piece of stone, by his eye, to the largest square figure which it will admit; forming blocks from half to six or eight tons weight; or more.

As quarrying developed around the northern edge of Portland, so did the difficulties of transport. A map of 1770 showed stone blocks piled at Quarry Head on the cliff top, with a steep road leading down to New Pier and King's Pier, where more stone awaited shipment. Such roads were in a terrible state by 1800, when horses or large blocks were dragged behind the stone carts to slow their descent. These difficulties were greatly relieved in 1826 when the Portland or Merchants' Railway was opened down to a quay at Castletown. This stimulated quarrying and in 1838 there were said to be 56 quarries and 240 quarrymen, of whom Messrs Stewards employed 138. Each 'quarry' was worked by a company of four or five men and a boy, all with their own tools.

There were changes in the Portland quarries after 1850. Convicts were brought to the island to quarry nearly 6 million tons of stone for the first Portland Breakwater of 1847–72. In 1865, the Weymouth & Portland Railway opened up markets in England, although shipments by sea continued apace. Many public buildings in London, including the Law Courts and National Gallery, were supplied with Portland stone and government works at dockyards, such as Portsmouth, also took stone from the private and convict quarries.

The second half of the century saw the establishment of new quarry firms and steam-powered stone sawmills and masonry works. Such was the Portland Stone Co. of 1872, with works at Victoria Square, Chiswell, taken over by F.J. Barnes in 1885. Five years later Webber & Pangbourne and John Pearce Stone Co. had works at Easton. The Bath Stone Firms arrived at

the turn of the century, gradually acquiring the assets of the older companies. This important firm became the Bath & Portland Stone Firms Co. Ltd in 1911, when it controlled half the total quarry workforce of 556 men.

Working a Coulter planing machine at the Bottomcombe stone works in 1930. The workyard also included massive frame saws, a stone lathe and a masonry department, all served by a siding from the railway at Easton.

BRITISH GEOLOGICAL SURVEY (NERC COPYRIGHT RESERVED)

In 1900 a railway extension was opened to Easton in the centre of the island, with sidings into an important stone mill at Bottomcombe. Quarrying continued to expand after the First World War when there was a demand for war memorials (including the Cenotaph) and thousands of war graves. Portland survived a slump in the early-1930s, one major contract being for London University. The Cap was crushed for concrete and aggregate, and other stone was crushed or burnt in limekilns. The Merchants' Railway had carried 93,133 tons in its peak year of 1904, but closed in October 1939. Portland stone was in great demand for rebuilding London and many other cities after the Second World War. In 1951 there were 296 quarrymen and 610 workers in the block and masonry works, but falling orders for expensive natural stone and the introduction of mechanisation caused the total workforce to fall to around 200 over the next twenty-five years. In 1960, the Bath & Portland Stone Firms and South Western Stone Co. Ltd amalgamated to become The Stone Firms Ltd, by far the major force on the island. After the Easton Railway closed in 1965 all stone left the island by road except for a few shipments from Castletown Pier.

Despite further amalgamations, the industry still thrives. With mechanisation now ruling in the quarries, cranes are no longer to be seen. There were once countless timber hand-cranes, followed by steam cranes in the 1880s and lattice-steel electric cranes by the 1930s. The old ways were ending in 1962 when there were still 17 cranes in Broadcroft

Advertisement for the Portland Stone Co. Ltd, steam sawmill proprietors, 1889.

Advertisement for Stewards & Co. Ltd, Portland Stone Masonry Works, 1889.

Suckthumb Quarry on Portland in April 1930, showing the narrow working area between the face and stack of waste blocks. A team of men works with each crane. The depth of overburden to be removed is immediately apparent.

Quarry, each worked by a team of six men. It is the traditional quarrying methods that are of interest – they hardly changed throughout two centuries.

Some early-nineteenth-century quarries were in the north, where there is much made-up ground in the Tout and Kingbarrow quarries. Tout Quarry *(SY 685727)* has the added interest of its sculpture park. Jonathon Lano was the quarry manager during a time of expansion and an impressive stone arch for a tramway is inscribed 'J.C. Lano 1854'. The sleeper blocks of a

Abandoned hand derrick crane at Suckthumb Quarry in 1984. After the quarry was infilled, this crane was restored and re-erected at Priory Corner.

The stone faces at Tout Quarry have been carved with modern sculptures, but an old wedge pit of the quarrymen can be seen on the ledge to the right of this climbing figure's hand.

Tout Quarry, Portland, showing Jonathon Lano's Arch amid vast piles of waste.

A detail of Lano's Arch in Tout Quarry, showing the date stone of 1854 and the superb drystone construction: a functional work of art made by practical quarrymen.

Merchants' Railway branch lead to a second Lano arch of 1862, which ran under Wide Street into Inmosthay Quarries. This and two other arches of the same period are now blocked. Tramway courses wind between tips of waste blocks, some with evidence of crane sites and others incorporating quarrymen's shelters. The few remaining quarry faces have marks of wedge-pits in the Roach and blasting holes in the Cap above. Waste was easily disposed of over the West Cliff, and the remains of tipping places survive all along the cliff top to the south, approached by tramway gullies cut through enormous banks of waste.

Waste-stone tipping places along the West Cliff of Portland.

The low cliffs around Portland Bill have been quarried since at least the 1850s. This area has well preserved quarry faces, all shallow and easily accessible. There are stone-cutting marks on a quarry face (SY 676684) and roughly squared or 'scappled' blocks lie among the waste. The Pulpit Rock was left by the quarrymen in the 1870s, but all else has been quarried away. There are two quarrymen's shelters built of massive blocks, and the stone sleepers of a tramway pass the Bill to an old shipping place where a replacement crane now launches fishing boats. The coast path to the northeast passes quarries with straight vertical faces, cut by steam-channelling machines in the 1920s and 1930s. These include Butts Quarry (SY 683688) and Cave Hole Quarry (SY 686691), with more at Sandholes (SY 687693) where there is now a single timber crane, latterly used for boat launching. Coastal quarries continue to Freshwater Bay, with evidence of waste-tipping tramways, quarried faces and the occasional crane sites.

This long quarry face near Portland Bill was formed by a steam-channelling machine in the early-twentieth century.

Purbeck is the second district with notable quarry archaeology. The famous Purbeck marble industry was really a medieval one, with polished stone sent to cathedrals and churches all over the country. Traces of old quarries follow the thin outcrop from Peveril Point to Worbarrow Tout, but there was new quarrying at Woodyhyde in the 1840s for restoring London's Temple church and at Blashenwell in the 1870s when Kingston church was financed by the Scott family. Other sites have been opened since for restoration work.

The main Purbeck stone beds were more important in later years, and a regular trade in kerbs and paving from Swanage to London was carried on from the seventeenth to the early-twentieth century. In the 1720s, Defoe wrote of:

> … *vast quarreys* [sic] *of stone, which is cut out flat, and us'd in London in great quantities for paving court-yards, alleys, avenues to houses, kitchins, footways on the sides of the high-streets, and the like.*

The different beds were worked extensively from Swanage to Worth Matravers, and many quarries are still active around Acton and Langton Matravers. Old shallow outcrop quarries or 'ridden holes' can be traced along the high ground westwards from the Durlston Country Park, but the deeper beds were worked underground in a 'quarr' accessed by an inclined shaft or 'slide'. Stone legs were built to support the roof and quarried stone was drawn on a 'trundle' to the foot of the slide and hauled to the surface by a horse or donkey attached to a long 'spack' (arm) turning a capstan held between two crab stones.

A quarry mouth drawn by Alfred Dawson depicts a typical Purbeck stone quarr of c.1880. The donkey attached to the spack turns the capstan to raise stone from the inclined slide, and the whole is sheltered by open-fronted quarr houses where masons dress the stone.

A Purbeck stone quarr near Swanage in October 1911. A trundle loaded with stone has been hauled to the surface by the mule attached to the spack and capstan.

BRITISH GEOLOGICAL SURVEY

The slide was paved at the top and a roller carried the chain over the edge. The capstan was set on a levelled mound of spoil and was partly enclosed by open-fronted 'quarr houses' where the stone was dressed. Quarrs were family businesses, each employing three or four men. There were 58 quarrs with 197 workers in 1907, but their numbers steadily declined to 13 quarrs in 1938 and two in 1950. Today, machines excavate open quarries, occasionally breaking into the old workings.

Crab stones hold the capstan and spack at Normans Quarr, Langton Matravers. The National Trust has restored this site with its small quarr houses where the stone was dressed. The shaft or slide is behind the camera.

The surface of Norman's Quarr *(SY 992789)* at Langton Matravers has been restored by the National Trust. It was worked from 1901–28 and has a typical capstan between two crab stones and two small quarr houses with stone-tiled roofs. Tramway rails from the inclined shaft are less typical. Old quarr houses beside filled-in shafts stand all around this area. A second capstan with a slide and trundle is in the Durlston Country Park *(SZ 032772)*.

Quarr capstan and crab stones preserved at the Durlston Country Park, near Swanage.

In 1750–52 the Trustees of Ramsgate Harbour employed 50 ships to carry 15,000 tons of stone from all the Purbeck quarries, and ashlar, facing blocks and backing were also shipped to Portsmouth and Dover. In 1756 John Smeaton noted underground quarries for paving stones but he was more interested in the underlying Purbeck-Portland beds along the coast from St Aldhelm's Head to Durlston Head, where they too were worked in underground galleries. He rejected this Purbeck 'cliffstone' in favour of Portland because it was inferior in colour, harder to work and a less reliable source, having fewer quarrymen and uncertain shipping conditions. Throughout the nineteenth century the quarries worked intermittently according to demand, but as trade diminished they became increasingly deserted.

The Pond Freestone was taken, but most galleries were quarried lower down in the Under Freestone, with uncut pillars left to support the roof of House Cap accompanied by 'legs' of stone blocks where necessary. Quarried blocks were shaped in the open or in the sheltered entrances of the galleries. The most accessible of all the cliffstone quarries are at Winspit, Seacombe, Hedbury and Dancing Ledge.

Winspit (*SY 976761* and *SY 978761*) was worked from at least 1719 and its wide galleries are notable for their slender supports. Stone was crushed for building roads and airfields in the Second World War after which some quarrying

continued until about 1950. Seacombe Quarry (*SY 984766*) was opened in the eighteenth century and there was a last attempt from 1923–31 when the Dorset Quarry Co. Ltd invested in compressed air drills and at least four steam cranes. Up to 36 men were employed in 1927, but the firm went into liquidation four years later. There are foundations on the quarry floor for an engine, compressor and stone saws, while bases and scattered cinders are evidence for steam cranes above the quarry face.

Stone could be carried inland only from Seacombe and Winspit for shipment from Swanage, but it required a hard climb. For other quarries the stone was shipped with difficulty from the cliffs, which adds an interesting dimension to their archaeology. It was largely a summer trade, involving multiple handling in risky conditions, but had

Twin legs support the roof at Seacombe Gallery. The marks of wedge-pits can be seen on the stone above the scale (0.2 metres).

Winspit Quarry, showing underground galleries and a higher ledge indicating the Pond Freestone.

The square-cut holes of a crane place on a ledge below the east quarries at Winspit.

Two branching rutways for carrying stone to a shipping place are still clearly visible at Dancing Ledge.

ceased by the end of the nineteenth century. The name Tilly Whim (*SZ 031769*) seems to refer to the crane type used. A king-post on the quarry edge supported a jib, which swung out to lower stone directly into a small craft or down to a flat ledge with a second loading crane. The stone was then taken out to a waiting sailing ship and once again transshipped. The evidence for over 20 crane sites at the quarries is a large square hole, with smaller holes for the anchor points and winch. A unique stone slab with square-cut holes overlies an earlier site at Hedbury Quarry (*SY 992768*), where stone was lowered to a shipping crane on a ledge below. Hedbury is depicted in a painting of about 1870 by H.T. Wells, showing a crane and a sailing ketch taking on stone from a small boat. The picture also shows the quarrier Thomas Chinchen Lander. A crane lowered stone to a ledge with a shipping place at the west end of Seacombe Quarry. The bottom crane position survives, and a line of square post-holes may have supported a platform or tramway across the ledge. Shipping was revived here in the late-1920s when a derrick loaded barges with stone for the training wall outside Poole Harbour.

Stones had to be carried across the widest ledges to the shipping crane, and two converging rutways were cut to guide the wheels of a 'horn cart' out to a crane at the end of the sea-washed

Dancing Ledge (*SY 997769*). At Winspit a rather crude rutway led to a crane site at a natural quay with a hazardous approach, while a longer one ran out to a crane only usable at low tide. There is a fifth rutway below a quarry at Blacker's Hole. These coastal rutways are not unique. Others, for example, served the alum industry between Saltburn and Scarborough in Yorkshire.

Of additional interest are apparent tally marks and carvings of period sailing vessels just inside gallery openings at Winspit, Halsewell, West Hedbury and other quarries. They may have been carved in idle moments while the quarry-men waited for calm loading conditions and perhaps they represent the vessels that shipped the stone.

The same Purbeck-Portland stone was worked high up on St Aldhelm's Head (*SY 962754*), leaving a curious pillar of uncut stone, and at St Aldhelm's Quarry (*SY 965761*), where building stone is still taken and W.J. Haysom & Son have a traditional stone-dressing yard. The only timber derrick left in a Dorset quarry stands derelict here. Further inland, Swanworth Quarry was developed for roadstone in the later-twentieth century.

St Aldhelm's Quarry is a traditional quarry with a stone-masonry yard. The disused timber derrick is the last historic crane standing in any Dorset quarry.

Other Dorset stones were of local importance. They are witnessed more by their widespread use in churches and older houses in towns and villages rather than by their quarries which are small, overgrown or even infilled. The Forest Marble and Inferior Oolites were quarried around Bridport, Beaminster, Sherborne and Stalbridge for building stone as well as lime burning. A freestone from the Corallian limestone was quarried around Marnhull and Todber in the Blackmoor Vale, where old shallow quarry faces survive around the edges of fields. An attempt was made in 1887 to exploit a narrow exposure of Portland limestone at Portesham (SY 610859), with a connecting incline from the Abbotsbury Railway. Little came of this and intermittent quarrying ceased altogether in about 1928. One of two limekilns survives near the abandoned quarry, and the line of the incline can be traced as a faint earthwork.

Widespread chalk pits were worked mostly for agriculture or lime burning, but in the absence of better stones the harder chalks were occasionally used for building. Many small pits are overgrown but larger ones with chalk faces include those at Maiden Newton or Shillingstone, both last worked for lime.

In north Dorset, the Upper Greensand was quarried for a building stone and roadmaking at Shaftesbury. The edges of almost every escarpment in this neighbourhood have overgrown quarries and dumps, although stone is seldom exposed. The long-abandoned Wilderness (ST 866224) just south of the town is the most accessible.

Workings for roadstone and aggregates were on a small scale in the nineteenth century but have grown into a major industry since the 1950s. Harder limestones and sandstones have all been exploited, while areas of valley gravels and Tertiary sands and gravels have been extensively worked in the southeast. Hundreds of small pits are evidence of sand and gravel digging for local needs, but commercial excavations have made a larger impact at places such as Warmell, or Binnegar near Wareham. Compared with hardstone quarries, none of these pits will leave behind much evidence of the mode of working.

4

❧ POTTERS' CLAY ❧

Many visitors to Purbeck will perhaps have relaxed at the famous Blue Pool *(SY 935833)* between Furzebrook and Norden. This is the most public of the old ball clay pits that were dug from the heath but now lie flooded and regenerated by vegetation. The attractive deep blue or green colour of the water in the Blue Pool is caused by the diffraction of light by suspended clay particles. This abandoned industrial site was opened in 1935 as a beauty spot and it was gradually surrounded by trees. A small museum provides an introduction to the development of the ball clay and pottery industries of the area.

Blue Pool was formed from a flooded nineteenth-century clay pit, and this popular and attractive site developed since 1935 proves that not all industry is ugly.

Ball clay became a major Dorset export to the Potteries from the late-eighteenth century. It is extremely fine-grained which gives it great 'plasticity'. The best clays fire white but there are many grades, some of which may appear the same as the best but will blister when fired because of minute traces of iron. The clay derives from a weathered source as far west as Devon, transported by rivers, sorted and deposited in 'lenses' among deltaic sands and gravels belonging to the Bagshot beds. Its main location is beneath the heaths just north of the Purbeck Hills, where it has been worked between Norden and West Creech, with other deposits to the east, and at Arne, Stoborough and Trigon, near Wareham.

It was first called pipeclay, because it was dug from at least 1619 for making clay tobacco pipes. By the end of the seventeenth century, when about 3000 tons were produced annually, surplus clay was shipped as far as Liverpool and Newcastle. Clay pipes made at Poole were sent to other ports, and as far as South Carolina in 1769 and Newfoundland until at least 1828. Another use was for sugar baking or refining.

Fine pottery, however, was the main market for the Purbeck clay. The growth in manufacturing china was linked with tea drinking and the pottery industry was drawn to Stoke-on-Trent in Staffordshire, where coal was available for firing the kilns. Blue and white clays from Purbeck and Devon had been sent to the Staffordshire potteries in 1719, but only later in the century was a regular trade established. Developments in the Purbeck ball clay fields advanced in the 1760s when, according to Hutchins, around 10,000 tons of potters' clay were exported from Poole to London, Liverpool and Glasgow. Some went via Selby to potteries at Leeds, but most was shipped to Liverpool, and thence to Staffordshire. Josiah Wedgwood established his famous Etruria pottery at Stoke in 1759 and the opening of the Trent & Mersey Canal in 1777 expanded the trade further, offering cheaper carriage of clay and finished wares.

Some of the early developments took place on the remote Arne peninsula, where pipeclay was dug in the early-eighteenth century. Thomas Hyde of Poole came to live here in the 1760s and obtained the rights in 1771 to dig clay on the estate of John Calcraft. He also entered an arrangement by which Wedgwood took 1400 tons of clay every year, but his activities ended in 1792. The clay dug from small pits at Arne was taken by donkeys along tracks to Hyde's Quay for shipment. Russel Quay on the deeper water of the Wareham Channel was adjacent to another clay pit.

At the same time, outsiders were becoming involved in the Purbeck industry and important developments took place on the heath in the Norden and Furzebrook area, from which clay was carried to Wareham for shipment. Pipeclay had been worked by the Brown family at Furzebrook since at least the 1660s, and William Pike of Chudleigh was active in this area a century later. He made an agreement with Wedgwood and others in 1791 to supply 1200 tons of ball clay over five years at a price of £600. In about 1795 Benjamin Fayle, a potter from London, opened pits at Norden, sending his clay along a track to a quay at Middlebere on a creek of Poole Harbour. Eleven years later he constructed an iron plateway to the quay, thus greatly increasing his export capacity and reducing transport costs. There are old clay pits of this period on both sides of the Wareham to Corfe road, although the main workings were to the west. In the 1860s Fayle & Co. opened a clay pit and works at Newton Heath (*SZ 012847*), from which the clay was sent on a railway and tipped into barges at Goathorn Pier.

William and John Pike were working clay pits near Creech from about 1815, while Watts, Hatherley & Burn were digging clay at Furzebrook in the 1830s and are believed to have opened the Blue Pool pit ten years later. They were bought out in 1850 by Pike Brothers, who were now expanding their operations and whose railway was built to Ridge Quay near Wareham in 1840. There was a clay-processing works at Ridge, to which the railway ran from pits around Furzebrook and the Blue Pool area. Horses were replaced by steam locomotives in 1866 and the line was diverted southwest at Furzebrook onto Creech Heath. However, Pike Brothers did not purchase Blue Pool until 1874. As new pits opened, the Pike Railway was extended to serve them until they were abandoned to the heath. Grange Gate was one of the largest pits, now flooded, but far from the scale of the Povington opencast currently worked at West Creech.

Exports at Poole from all the clay pits were 14,796 tons in 1802, while ten years later they were said to be 16–20,000 tons with another 3–4000 tons of inferior clay mostly sent to Bristol and London for brown stoneware jars. An extra 2½cwt was allowed for every ton because of the weight loss as the clay dried. Exports had risen to 62,932 tons in 1859, of which most came from Purbeck. The clay was sent to ports as far away as Bristol, Cardiff, Chester, Hull, Liverpool, Sunderland and Whitehaven, as well as to Germany, Netherlands, Belgium and Spain. By this date rail was used for some consignments to British potters and increasing quantities were being taken locally by the newly established tile and pottery works in Poole.

Wedgwood was not the only famous potter trading with Dorset, for ball clay was shipped to Royal Worcester, Minton and others. Doulton & Co. of Lambeth became directly involved and in 1907 were raising over 18,000 tons from clay pits at Lake, Hamworthy (*SY 981908*), where they employed 50 men. By this date the range of products for which the clay was used worldwide had expanded to include fine stoneware pottery, jars, bottles, chemical apparatus, sanitary fittings, electrical insulators and drainpipes, as well as the local tiles and 'every kind of architectural pottery'.

Norden (*SY 958828*) had become Fayle & Co.'s headquarters, where exchange sidings were made after the Swanage Railway was opened in 1885. After the Goathorn Railway was extended to Norden in 1905, all clay was shipped from the deeper water at Goathorn Pier and the old Middlebere Tramway was closed. The pier and railway to Goathorn fell out of use after the Newton pit closed in the late-1930s, but some lines continued to serve the exchange sidings at Norden. Pike Brothers closed their railway to Ridge Quay in 1943 but the upper branches from the pits continued to serve a clay depot at Furzebrook, where there was a siding from the Swanage Railway. After the Second World War, the two main clay firms merged in 1949 as Pike Brothers, Fayle & Co. Ltd, and in the following year had a workforce of 267 men. Norden was abandoned in favour of Furzebrook as the main processing works. The firm continued throughout the 1950s and 60s until E.C.C. Ball Clays Ltd bought it out in 1969.

Traditionally the clay was weathered in the open for six months to improve its plasticity before processing, but Pike Brothers, Fayle & Co. Ltd introduced a faster method of artificial weathering at the Furzebrook works (*SY 932840*). Here the clay was crushed and shredded to a size most suited for bulk shipment or handling. Clays were graded and blended and customers could receive products as dried and granulated clay (a method developed by the company in 1956), powdered clay or air-floated clay, all with different moisture contents. The clays were graded, with names such as K, Fayles Blue, No.1, TLD, 71CW, PK, No.4 and PK. High plasticity and strength was sought for many products including floor tiles, ceramic whitewares, sanitary wares, refractory products such as retorts, kiln furniture and crucibles, large porcelain insulators for the electrical industry, and fillers in synthetic rubber, fertilisers and animal feeds.

The industrial archaeology of this successful industry is mostly well hidden from view under heathland or woodland vegetation. The ball clay, which may be as little as 10 feet below the surface, was first worked in open pits, the overburden of sands and unwanted clays being cast aside. The pits were dug by hand using a 'tubal', a long spade which cut out blocks about a foot square. In 1882, C.E. Robinson described the working of a 'china-clay' pit at Corfe, with an illustration drawn by Alfred Dawson:

Here is a wide uncovered excavation, the rubbish overlying the clay not being many yards in thickness. The steep sides are being cut away in steps by men with spades, and are charmingly tinted, light pink, bright yellow, gray, and white, according to the varieties of the clay. As they are cut, the square lumps of the plastic material are slid in a wet state along a smooth plank, towards a truck, into which they are lifted by a man with an iron prong. From the ground-level above an engine hauls the loaded trucks up an inclined tramway, and when it has leisure from this employment, is busily engaged in sawing out timber props and sleepers. The whole scene, on a fine day, is animated and pretty; but in wet weather there must be pleasanter occupations than the constant handling and treading of slippery adhesive clay.

From the early-1800s, prospectors have drilled test bores to locate new clay deposits and deter-

was raised on supports so that the clay could be tipped into hoppers beneath the floor for despatch into railway wagons and, in the later days, lorries.

The pit-head building at Norden Clay Mine showing the raised winch house and clay bins with the inclined shaft beyond.

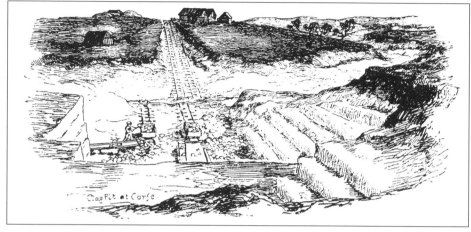

Clay pit at Corfe: a drawing by Alfred Dawson of a working described in 1882 by C.E. Robinson in A Royal Warren or Picturesque Rambles in the Isle of Purbeck.

mine their depth, thickness and extent. The open pits were worked down to about 50 feet, but for anything deeper it was more economic to sink a shaft. Robinson mentioned a 'china-clay mine' just northeast of Creech Barrow, and five years later, 56 clay miners were recorded working for Pikes at 'Furzy Ground'. The earliest mines had vertical shafts to a depth of about 120 feet, with winding gear and a timber headframe at the surface. At some mines, iron cylinders were sunk in sections through weak ground to form the shaft.

Drift mines were developed with an inclined shaft descending as far as 300 feet. Underground, the clay is surprisingly hard and dry, and the miners first used a double-sided adze to cut it out before pneumatic spades made the job easier. Up to 20 feet of clay was left untouched to form a watertight ceiling, supported by timber props which were allowed to collapse as mining advanced. Only two men could work at the confined clay face, one cutting and the other loading stout wooden trams which were assembled at the shaft bottom to be winched to the surface. The surface building had a winch opposite the incline and the whole

Excavating the clay face in Norden Mine. This is 1996 and a pneumatic spade is used, but otherwise the techniques are little changed.

The Greenspecks Clay Mine was well hidden and its inclined shaft appeared to vanish into the forest.

By 1971, there were still ten mines and eight pits, mostly well concealed; the Greenspecks Mine for example was hidden in woodland and yet adjacent to a public road. The Norden drift mine *(SY 949827)* was the last worked by E.C.C. Ball Clays. It was sunk to about 200 feet, with two underground levels, and a second shaft was opened four years before the mine closed in 2001.

A clay miner with a loaded wagon underground in Norden Mine.

Timber pit props outside Norden Clay Mine.

5

❧ SHALE AND OTHER FUELS ❧

Kimmeridge shale was exploited long before the Industrial Revolution and its unusual history dates far back into prehistory. Early Bronze-Age folk carved and polished beads, rings and even cups from this dark shale and by the late Iron Age it was being dug from the cliffs and turned on pole lathes for armlets. Several 'industrial' sites have been recognised, as at Rope Lake Head, and more are known from the Roman period, including Norden which is some distance away. The waste shale cores from the lathes were picked up over the centuries and known as 'Kimmeridge Coal Money'. More spectacular are the Roman shale furniture legs and tops discovered at Dorchester and other local sites, while finds from Bath, Silchester and St Albans indicate there was a wide demand.

Within the exposed cliff sequence at Kimmeridge are two main beds of bituminous oil shale, the Blackstone and the Bubbicum, known as 'Kimmeridge Coal' which was for centuries burned locally for domestic heating. Householders benefited further, for its ash and the contents of cesspits rendered the 'soil light and fertile, and producing luxuriant vegetation.'

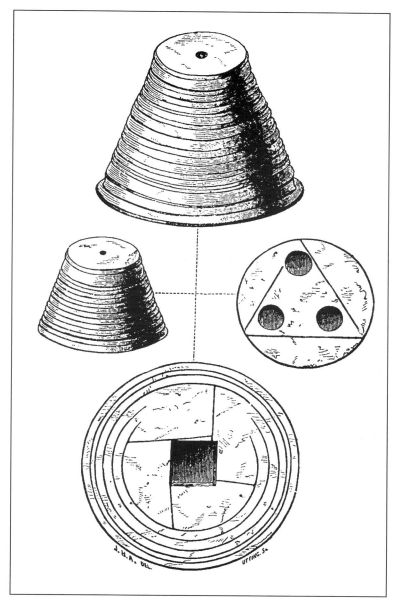

Kimmeridge coal money, the shale discs discarded after turning amulets and rings on a lathe in Iron-Age times, illustrated in John Hutchins' History of Dorset.

Kimmeridge shale was a source of alum, a chemical used in preparing mordants for dyeing and calico-printing, preserving skins, candle making and pharmacy. Sir William Clavell's alum works at Kimmeridge had to be closed, so he established a glassworks in 1617, but again his luck ran out and he was forced to dismantle it after only six years. Interestingly, the glass furnace was fuelled by oil shale, which Coker warned 'in burneing yeelds such an offensive Savour and extraordinarie Blacknesse, that the People labouring about those Fire are more like Furies than Men'. It was perhaps fortunate for these men that Clavell was made to close the works.

After a long period of neglect, the greatest industrial activity at Kimmeridge came in the nineteenth century, with several attempts to exploit the oil shale commercially. In 1848, the Bituminous Shale Co. was registered with a capital of £25,000 and built a tramway to carry the shale from clifftop excavations at Cuddle to a pier for shipping to their works at Weymouth. Here the shale was distilled in retorts to produce varnish, lubricating grease, naphtha, pitch and paraffin wax. It was said that the residuum from the retorts made a good fertiliser. However, there were difficulties with the lease at Kimmeridge, the process was imperfect and the factory with its offensive smells was considered a nuisance, and the company was wound up in 1854. In that year Ferguson & Muschamp built a works at Wareham to produce a manure from the shale. It was also found that the product prevented wire-worm, grub and 'other noxious insects.' The shale was said to yield 7½ gallons of naphtha, 10 gallons of lubricating oil, 1cwt of pitch and 11½cwt of residue, as well as 'some fine white paraffin wax and gas.' However, the operation was soon abandoned.

Wanostrocht & Co., with a number of Frenchmen including Marshal Pelisser, built a new 'mineral oil works' at Northport, Wareham, and proceeded with development work at Kimmeridge from 1858–60, including the driving of adits into the cliffs and the erection of two piers connected to tramways. Successful marketing of the shale resulted in the export of 1149 tons in 1858 to Australia, Boston, Dieppe, Marseilles, New York and Philadelphia, with a similar tonnage shipped in 1859. The most unusual contract, and one which failed, would have supplied shale to light the streets of Paris. After getting into difficulties a few years later, the Wareham Oil & Candle Co. took over, but the works burnt down. In about 1876 the Sanitary Carbon Co. used the residual coke as an antiseptic deodoriser and decolouriser. The sanitary carbon was also applied to the purification of sewage and was used effectively at places including Hurstpierpoint in Sussex, Malling and Snodland in Kent, and Burghley House at Stamford.

'The Kimmeridge Coal Pit', drawn by Alfred Dawson, shows a timber crane with a crab-winch used to haul oil shale to the top of the cliff where two men are bagging and weighing the product.

In 1879 De Gelle & Co. took over and formed the Kimmeridge Oil & Carbon Co. The final significant operation at Kimmeridge was from 1883–90 when the shale was mined from the cliffs at Clavell's Hard and the Manfield Shaft, and carried on a mile-long tramway to a timber pier.

There are some remains of industrial activity below Clavel's Tower at Kimmeridge and the cliffs to the east. Along the coastal footpath an overgrown cutting ending in the cliff edge at Cuddle *(SY 912783)* is evidence of the 1848 workings and the course of the tramway leads off through a field below the tower. Further east, the Manfield Shaft *(SY 917783)* has been flattened but its position in a field is marked by a blackish area in the soil after ploughing. There is a quarried ledge halfway down the cliff at Clavell's Hard *(SY 920778)*. Adits into workings here and along

The quarried ledge at Clavell's Hard was the scene of oil shale workings.

the cliffs have collapsed long ago, although some tramway rails protrude from the crumbling cliffs.

There was renewed interest at Kimmeridge in 1917 when the Department for the Development of Mineral Resources (Ministry of Munitions) drilled three boreholes to determine the extent and potential of the oil shale. The main Blackstone shale band, about 2-feet 6-inches thick, was found to yield around 40 gallons of oil per ton, but the high sulphur content would make distillation 'very offensive' and the product inferior. There were an estimated 12 million tons of Blackstone beneath 2900 acres of land.

Twenty miles westward, Portesham was destined to become another Kimmeridge when bituminous shale was discovered by W. Manfield in the 1850s at Portesham Dairy, but the shallow workings became flooded after only a few tons had been removed. In 1877 the main outcrop was exposed in a railway cutting east of Portesham Station and about 2000 tons of this 'coal' were mixed with clay and burnt for railway ballast. In 1883 the Manfield Shaft was sunk 189 feet, cutting rich oil shale beds at 46 feet and 137 feet. An incline of 1 in 4 was cut to the shaft from the outcrop next to the railway. Some 100 tons of shale were transported to retorts in Scotland at this time and again in 1903, but it was found to be inferior and containing too much sulphur. The 25-inch Ordnance Survey map for 1901 shows a small engine house at the Manfield shale pit, but today the site is just an overgrown mound (SY 609856). As at Kimmeridge, boreholes were made in 1917 to assess the potential oil shale outcrop around Corton and German prisoners of war were involved in these attempts. A trial at Westham, Weymouth, was even less successful. Bituminous shale is also said to have been dug for fuel between the tide marks at Castletown, Portland.

The story of true coal as a fuel in Dorset is not a long one. Although Kimmeridge shale was often called 'coal', the nearest to true coal was lignite. When available, both were used locally and both were unpleasant to burn. In 1815 Stevenson wrote that at Kimmeridge the 'coal' gave out a sulphurous smell and strong bright light, and was 'chiefly used in ovens, and by the poor people.' Lignite, a poorly formed type of coal, occurs occasionally in the Bagshot beds under the Purbeck heaths. In parts of the sand above the ball clay in the pits around Norden, Stevenson referred to 'a small vein of bad sulpherous [sic] coal, barely worth burning.' A Mr Hall of Hilton informed Stevenson that slaty coal was to be found 'in great abundance' at Ansty, where 'it

burns with a bright and lively flame, but yields, in its combustion, an exceeding disagreeable smell; so that it is not made use of for fuel.' He felt good coal might be found below.

There were several attempts to find coal at depth in the Sherborne area from about 1690 until 1740. They were still looking in 1815 when, according to Stevenson, some gentlemen had applied to Lord Digby for permission to seek coal at Sherborne, 'as a person skilled in mineralogy had observed the crop of good coal appear to the day.' Nothing was found. There were other attempts between Bedchester and Fontmell Magna to the south of Shaftesbury in about 1800 and a few years earlier Sir John Webb had made a coal trial on Canford Heath near Poole, sinking a bore to 280 feet into the chalk below. The greatest trial boring was made in 1901 by Vivian's Boring & Exploration Co. in a valley northwest of Lyme Regis, reaching a depth of 1302 feet. No coal was found but this very deep bore was of geological interest, passing through the Lias and Rhaetic beds into the Keuper marl.

The lack of coal in Dorset had consequences for its industries. Coal had to be carried by expensive land carriage into the inland parts of north Dorset from the Somerset coalfield. This undoubtedly encouraged the attempts to find coal in Dorset, while the failed Dorset & Somerset Canal of the late-eighteenth century was intended to relieve the situation. The coastal parts of southeast Dorset received coal by sea from Newcastle, and west Dorset took Welsh coal. Some coal was carried surprisingly far inland from the ports but much of this trade was lost to the railways after the 1850s.

Oil is a twentieth-century industry. Dorset now has the largest onshore oilfield in Britain, developed since the discovery at Wytch Farm in 1973, but the story of oil exploration dates back at least to the 1930s. Oil seepages along the coast, for example at Bran Point near Ringstead and other locations on Purbeck, were brought to the attention of the D'Arcy Exploration Co. A programme of drilling was undertaken from 1936–9, starting at Poxwell, then Ringstead and at Broad Bench, Kimmeridge. None of these found oil, although much was learnt of the geological structures hidden deep below. The Second World War held up further investigations, but the prospectors returned in the 1950s and were rewarded when British Petroleum drilled near Gaulter Gap at Kimmeridge to discover oil at a depth of 1816 feet. The well head with its 'nodding donkey' pump has been a feature at Kimmeridge Bay since 1959.

Nodding donkey pump at the Kimmeridge oil well where drillers struck lucky in 1959.

6

❧ IRONSTONE WORKING ❧

Metal mining was never one of Dorset's industries with the exception of scattered attempts to work iron ore. Hengistbury Head (then in Hampshire!) was the only place to see any large-scale exploitation in the nineteenth century. Undoubtedly, ironstone from the sandy beds of the head was exploited in the Iron Age when there was a significant trading port on the shore of Christchurch Harbour. Four main broken beds of ironstone are exposed in the crumbling sea cliff of Warren Hill. Eroded blocks that had fallen onto the beach below protected the coastline from the action of the sea, but these 'doggers' were an easy source of ironstone and there was an attempt to work them on a commercial scale in the period 1848–70.

In 1848 John Edward Holloway, a coal and general merchant of Christchurch, obtained a lease to work the ironstone from Sir George Gervis, lord of the manor who claimed the rights of the foreshore. Holloway and a partner from South Wales set up the Hengistbury Head Mining Co. and their workers were soon collecting ironstone from the shore beneath the cliffs. The larger doggers were broken up on the beach and carried away by horse and cart to be shipped for smelting in South Wales. To aid this operation a tramway was laid from the south beach around to a shipping place on the north side of the headland. By 1854 it was said that around 40 tons a day were being removed, with Holloway employing up to 200 men here. A total of 4000 tons of ore were awaiting shipment.

However, the removal of the natural protection afforded by the doggers caused the rapid erosion of the soft headland behind at such an alarming rate (up to 100 yards by 1854) that the Admiralty was petitioned to stop Holloway's operations there. The Admiralty ordered that stones should not be removed from below the high-water mark. The mining company eventually ceased work in 1870, but the damage was done. The cliffs continued to be eroded, with the spit at the entrance to Christchurch Harbour growing ever eastwards, to the detriment of navigation.

Attention was also turned to the north and west sides of Warren Hill where the Hengistbury Head Mining Co. opened deep stepped excavations into the soft ground, known as the Batters. There were no underground mines, but a deep cutting was begun in about 1856 across Warren Hill almost as far as the seaward cliff. Explosives were used to cut down into the main ironstone beds and two fatal accidents were reported in 1857, one while blasting and the other due to a landslip. This narrow 'ironstone canyon' (SZ 176906) remains as a monument to this enterprise, with the lower part deep and overgrown and the upper end flooded with a pond held behind a dam of ironstone doggers.

The quarry pond has been created in a deep gully excavated for ironstone across Warren Hill at Hengistbury Head.

The quarry pond at Hengistbury Head, with ironstone doggers in the foreground in the dam construction.

The ore was shipped from Holloway's Dock, an artificial channel cut through the saltings and mud to a pool in the shelter of the Head. Holloway had his own fleet of barges towed by a paddle-tug; his printed coal price notices illustrated the tug towing four barges, all five vessels with a square sail. Having first brought coal from Southampton to Christchurch, the barges, which would have otherwise returned empty to South Wales, went back with iron ore to be transshipped to the colliers. Taking ironstone as cargo or ballast was a means of keeping freight rates lower than they might have been.

In contrast, the pretty landscape around Abbotsbury seems the most unlikely place for iron ore working. Yet there was a serious attempt to extract ore in 1872 when the Earl of Ilchester granted a licence giving Charles Moore of Bath the right to sink shafts, erect sheds and machinery, and lay tramways. The Bridport Railway even considered building a connecting line, and a tramway to Upwey was also proposed, but nothing came of the mining. The Abbotsbury Iron Ore, described by the Geological Survey as 'crumbling reddish-brown ironshot ore', outcrops in Red Lane where there are old shallow workings. A sample from the north side of Linton Hill contained up to 36 per cent metallic iron, but the ore contained too much silica to have been worked commercially. The ironstone beds of up to 20-feet thickness were estimated to cover 256 acres. There is a small exposure of iron-bearing strata in Blind Lane up the hill to the north of Abbotsbury *(SY 576856)*.

Holloway's Dock is still visible where a cut was made through the saltings for the shipment of ironstone from Hengistbury Head.

7

❧ LIME BURNING ❧

A small picnic site up a narrow lane above Abbotsbury has an outstanding view and the Bishop's Limekiln *(SY 574861)*. Already disused by 1880, this is one of the few named limekilns from nearly 370 known sites in Dorset. Why were there so many and what was their purpose?

Wherever there was limestone or chalk available, most Dorset parishes had at least one limekiln to produce lime for agriculture and building mortar by the late-eighteenth century. This very rural industry was declining rapidly by 1900 in the face

The Bishop's Limekiln near Abbotsbury.

of agricultural depressions, competition from large commercial lime burners, and the introduction of Portland cement for building. Nevertheless, some larger kilns were built from the 1920s to 1950s and, unlike in most other counties, lime burning in Dorset continued down to the very end of the twentieth century.

When chalk or limestone (calcium carbonate) is burnt at 900°C, carbon dioxide is released to leave behind quicklime (calcium oxide) which reacts violently with water to form slaked or hydrated lime. Agricultural lime was the most important use and became widespread among farmers in the late-eighteenth century. The earlier agricultural improvers considered lime to be a manure which was used alongside chalk and marl dug from numerous small pits. In 1793 John Claridge wrote that 'a great deal of lime is used as a manure, and twenty hogsheads of four bushels each, per acre, is esteemed a good dressing.' Twenty years later, Stevenson found that 'lime is much used in the Vale of Blackmoor, in the neighbourhood of Sherborne, Cheddington, Beaminster, Bridport, and along the coast from Burton to Abbotsbury, Fleet and Weymouth.' Lime was taken from the kiln in lumps which were allowed to slake in the corner of a field

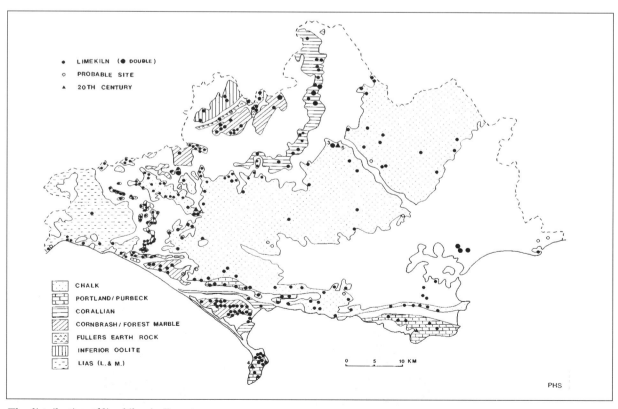

LIMEKILN (● DOUBLE)
o PROBABLE SITE
▲ 20TH CENTURY

CHALK
PORTLAND/PURBECK
CORALLIAN
CORNBRASH/FOREST MARBLE
FULLERS EARTH ROCK
INFERIOR OOLITE
LIAS (L.& M.)

0   5   10 KM

PHS

The distribution of limekilns in Dorset.

before being harrowed and ploughed in. Farmers applied the lime mostly in the spring or autumn. This soluble form of calcium neutralises soil acidity to encourage the action of bacteria which render fertilisers and other nutrients available for plant growth. It also improves the texture of soil. Today, ground chalk or limestone is the most usual agricultural 'lime' dressing which, although less soluble, is far cheaper and easier to handle.

Lime was used for building, by adding slaked lime to sand, and there are medieval records of lime burning for work at Corfe Castle. Although most builders chose the more convenient Portland cement when it became available in the second half of the nineteenth century, lime continued to be sold to the trade in small quantities and it has even seen a revival for restoration work on old properties in recent years. Lime for stucco work and plaster was burnt in Purbeck. For the cottager, lime ash was used for laying hard floors; whitewash was made from lime and whiting. Victorian water suppliers used lime for softening water, while a limekiln close to Weymouth gasworks in 1866 probably made lime for purifying coal gas. A bushel of lime could treat up to 10,000 cubic feet of gas.

The earliest existing structure in Dorset is a pit kiln at Wytch Heath *(SY 974846)*, dating from agricultural improvements of the early-eighteenth century. Excavations demonstrated that it had a single flue with raking pit. It was an intermittent type, which was fired and allowed to cool before discharge. At nearby Ower, a lease of 1730 gave William Cooper 'the free liberty and priviledge of making errecting and setting up a lime kiln', and three years later another lease refers to the 'new… lime kilne.' Unusually, these small kilns were sited on the heath to which the chalk for burning would have to been carried for some distance.

There are a few pointers to limekilns from the mid-eighteenth century onwards. For example, John Hutchins mentioned a limekiln near St Edward's Bridge at Corfe Castle in 1753, while Isaac Taylor's Map of Dorsetshire, 1765, showed a limekiln outside Blandford Forum. A single limekiln to the south of Church Knowle was marked on the Ordnance Survey one-inch map, surveyed in 1805–07. In the 1820s, limekilns are known from documentary sources and maps at Charmouth, Christchurch, Lyme Regis and Stourpaine. In February 1825 one Thomas Hardy (the author's grandfather, who was a builder) advertised 'good well-burnt lime' at Slyer's Lane Lime Kiln near Dorchester, although its precise location remains a mystery. Some parish Tithe Maps in about 1840 marked limekilns, depending

on the whim of the surveyor, but field names such as 'Limekiln Ground' suggest the sites.

Trade directories recorded very few lime burners or merchants. For example in 1903 there were only 11 in Dorset, yet contemporary Ordnance Survey maps show at least 109 limekilns still in use. The conclusion must be that most small kilns were run by farmers for their own purposes. Henry Smith of Stoke Abbott was only listed as a farmer in 1895, yet surviving ledgers in the Dorset Record Office show he was selling lime from his Waddon Hill limekiln to many customers around the district.

The majority of rural limekilns were abandoned during the early-twentieth century, but there was new activity by commercial lime burners. At Swanworth Quarry, Purbeck, two steel cylinder kilns were operated from about 1925. Two large kilns were built of concrete at Whitesheet Hill *(SY 586980)*, near Maiden Newton, in the 1950s by Soil Fertility Ltd, while the last limekiln on Portland, at Inmosthay *(SY 690725)*, ceased in 1959. Of special note, the Shillingstone Lime & Stone Co. Ltd built kilns of traditional design and installed a modern hydration plant in the 1930s at a chalk pit on Shillingstone Hill *(ST 823099)* and their last kiln was burning in 2000 when the operation closed.

Bagging lime at the Shillingstone limeworks in 1935.

The usual Dorset limekilns were the draw type, which could burn for weeks if a continuous supply of lime was required. The survivors are difficult to date but most must belong to the early to mid-nineteenth century. A typical kiln was built into a bank with a protective wall around the kiln head. Construction was of stone or brick, with thick insulating walls. The brick-lined pot was circular, with sides tapering towards the base. The main feature was a single draw arch in the front wall to give access to the draw hole at the base of the pot. The draw hole provided draught

Abandoned overhead cableway above two kilns at Shillingstone. The cableway, powered by an electric winch, once brought chalk down from the quarry on the hillside above.

and the means of extracting the burnt lime. Above, small poking holes were for inserting an iron bar to test or dislodge the charge. Most kilns were single, with very few banks of two or more.

For fuel, the medieval Corfe Castle accounts mention brushwood, timber and 'sea-coals'. Furze or faggots were used where there was a good local supply, and even lignite may have been tried at Wytch Heath in the eighteenth century. Coal brought coastwise to the Dorset ports was available in their immediate hinterlands. In 1796 William Marshall referred to lime burning 'with Welch culm; at least in the Bridport quarter.' Culm was broken anthracite, mixed with small coal dust. In 1893, Neath culm was shipped to a Somerset port such as Bridgwater or Highbridge and thence by rail to a siding at Crewkerne Station, where it was purchased for Henry Smith's limekiln at Waddon Hill. It was easier and cheaper to get this fuel via the railways than through the harbour at West Bay. Coke from gasworks was used in some limekilns in the early-twentieth century.

Broken limestone or chalk was delivered by cart or barrow to the kiln head and tipped into the pot for burning. The stone and fuel were loaded in the proportions of four to one. It was important to have voids between the stones for the even distribution of heat and to allow the escape of harmful gases. As burning proceeded and the lime was taken from the draw hole, the charge sank down and more stone and fuel were added. It might take three or four days to burn the lime. Controlling the burning was an art because over-burning was wasteful in fuel and might vitrify the stone, while underburning produced an unburnt core. The draught could be regulated through the iron draw hole door, if fitted, and the poking holes. The kiln top was usually left open.

Recorded fatalities were due mostly to the effects of inhaling 'carbonic gas' but children were the saddest victims. On 1 August 1832, four boys aged six to eight climbed over the wall of a Langton Herring limekiln to get down to the heated limestone, where they were overcome and suffocated. Another tragedy occurred one morning in October 1863, when fifteen-year-old James Burt of Shroton fell into the burning kiln at Melbury Hill, while his father and the lime burner were loading a wagon with lime.

A lean-to or gable roofed shed was commonly attached to the front of the kiln to protect the working area from the weather when the burnt lime was being bagged, barrelled or stored in bulk. Most lime sheds had wide doors so the lime could be loaded direct to a cart or wagon. Good examples survive at Bell House, Loders (SY 499949), and at Willwood, Kingston (SY 948798), but there is often some trace even where a lime shed has been demolished. The most unusual of the Langton Herring limekilns is in a field near Langton Cross (SY 622825), where the draw arch is approached through an artificial tunnel instead of a lime shed. A similar feature is found at Upwey (SY 670850).

A good example of a lime shed is attached to this limekiln at Bell House, near Loders, in west Dorset.

This well preserved limekiln at Langton Herring has an unusual tunnel approach to the draw arch instead of the more usual lime shed.

In the 1790s lime cost 4½d per bushel and in 1815 Stevenson reported that at Sherborne lime was sold for 6d per bushel, although 'it is supposed farmers can burn it for their own use for 2½d or 3d a bushel.' Prices were similar in the 1890s, when lime from Waddon Hill was sold at 1s 8d per hogshead, or 5d a bushel. Stevenson observed that lime was 'carried down very steep hills in panniers by asses,' and it must have been a busy scene when a limekiln was being discharged. Carts were used where roads allowed. In the late-nineteenth century lime was bought at Waddon Hill by farmers and builders in the district. For example, William Tucker of Park Farm, Chideock (8 miles away), carted off 20 hogsheads daily over 28 days from December 1889–January 1890. This represents three tons a day, enough to lime one acre if spread as recommended by Stevenson.

With few exceptions, limekilns were located on outcrops of limestones throughout Dorset, with the greatest number on the chalk, particularly the steep escarpments. The distribution shows marked concentrations, such as on the Inferior Oolite in west Dorset, Cornbrash at Langton Herring and Chickerell, Cornbrash and Fuller's Earth around Sherborne, Corallian limestone near Marnhull, and the limestone on Portland. In the east, large kilns on the heaths at Poole were related to the production of building lime for the growing towns of Poole and Bournemouth.

The rural limekilns were sited in or near a small quarry. Occasional kilns were freestanding structures, with a loading ramp, but most were built into a bank so they could be loaded from the top. A good example is the kiln at Bucknowle (SY 945822) near Church Knowle which stands just below a chalk quarry in the steep ridge of the Purbeck Hills. Others cut into a hillside required only a front wall and draw arch. Most were rectangular in plan, although one at North Poorton (SY 512980) is a rounded type. Local stone was used for the walls and draw arches, although details were finished in brick if the stone was unsuitable. Some brick arches were built to a very high standard, as seen around Langton Herring.

The draw arch is the most striking feature of a limekiln but its style is too varied to recognise the hand of a single builder. Rounded arches, in stone or brick, are found throughout Dorset and one of the finest is at Bucknowle, mentioned above. Pointed arches, with straight or slightly curved sides, are mostly in west Dorset and may represent a regional style, or possibly an earlier form. There are good examples at Limekiln Hill (SY 540870) above West Bexington, New Lane at Swyre (SY

The tall stone kiln at Limekiln Hill above West Bexington.

521880), Bredy North Hill at Burton Bradstock (SY 511907), Bothenhampton (SY 471915), and in an old quarry at West Cliff (SY 454909) above West Bay. A limekiln at South Barn (SZ 008780) on Purbeck also has this type of arch. There are timber lintels in north Dorset, as at Caundle Wake, while the Bishop's Limekiln at Abbotsbury has two lintels.

The kiln pot was built of header-bonded bricks, many of which show signs of vitrification from the heat. Only two kilns are known to have had firebricks. A small restored kiln at Caundle Wake (ST 700128) in the Blackmoor Vale is one of only two in Dorset to be lined with stone and not brick. It may have an early date. Most pots are rubble-filled, but open examples give a good impression of their shape, as at Bothenhampton, Bucknowle or Limekiln Hill.

The Bucknowle Limekiln at Church Knowle has an impressive draw arch and a burner's bothy (left). It was conserved by the Dorset Countryside Volunteers in the early 1980s.

The lime burner had to be in attendance at critical hours and sometimes a special shelter was provided. The most convincing is the 'bothy' built within the structure of the Bucknowle kiln at Church Knowle, complete with a Gothic window opening and a fireplace. It was refloored when the limekiln was restored by the Dorset Countryside Volunteers in the early 1980s and is unique in Dorset.

The modest limekiln represents a rural industry that came and went within 250 years. A few limekilns have been restored but more deserve some form of recognition or preservation. They are a valued part of Dorset's countryside heritage.

The restored limekiln at Bothenhampton.

8

❦ CEMENT MANUFACTURING ❦

Cement making was carried on to a limited extent in Dorset, but never replaced the limekilns. The building that now houses a visitor centre and café beside the beach car park at Charmouth *(SY 364930)* is a surviving part of a cement works. This mill was built close to the shore from which cement stones were gathered, and it worked from about 1850 until 1867. It was powered by a small steam engine, and two granite millstones lying on the slope behind were used for grinding the cement in the manufacturing process. Two limekilns behind the cement mill may have been earlier in date, but were probably incorporated into the works; just part of one survives today. Charmouth had a third limekiln in 1841, set in the cliffs on the east side of the beach, but it has been destroyed long since by coastal erosion.

The building of the old Charmouth cement works is now a café and heritage centre close to the shore.

These two granite millstones, hardly noticed by visitors using the seat, are survivors from the Charmouth cement works.

There was a much larger cement factory just along the coast at Lyme Regis. Hydraulic cement was made here, using Blue Lias limestone picked up from the beach and quarried from the cliffs behind. These argillaceous (clayey) limestones were exploited for hydraulic cement, which has the ability to set under water and is therefore useful in works such as dock construction. At first, the stones were carried by small boat to the harbour at Lyme where they were sent away mainly as ballast on ships. From 1853 this industry was aided by a narrow-gauge horse-drawn tramway that ran onto the wharf in the harbour from the site of the cement factory. The factory was at work from about 1865, rebuilt in 1901 and closed in 1914. There was a small brick kiln and a disused limekiln nearby in 1888, but seemingly unrelated. Two tall disused chimneys of the abandoned cement works were demolished by the Royal Engineers in 1936 and the site became an RAF air-sea rescue station from 1937–64. Later converted to an outdoor activities centre, it now houses a boatbuilding school.

A third cement works was set up at Ridge, near Wareham, shortly after 1870 by Thomas Page Powell. The main raw material was chalk marl which was quarried from pits along the summit of Cocknowle Hill and sent down a steep tramway incline to the bottom where it was loaded into horse wagons and taken by road to Ridge. The cement-making process was described in 1881. After mixing and grinding, the marl was passed through a pug mill to be formed into bricks which were stacked on drying racks. When ready they were burnt in the kilns with coke fuel until reduced to clinkers.

This material was then crushed to the size of walnuts and raised to a hopper by an elevator. Finally it was sieved (1600 meshes per square inch) weighed and packed in casks. Power came from a horizontal condensing engine with a 4-ton flywheel, with steam raised in a Cornish boiler, both supplied by Stephen Lewin of Poole. At a similar date C.E. Robinson mentioned a tall chimney, bottle-shaped kilns and a long 'barn-like structure of brick and tiles, form part of the cement factory, where a pale-green marly substance … is roasted and ground into cement.' In 1900 Powell was advertising 'Portland Cement of the greatest strength and best quality … as supplied to Government, Gas, Water, Sewage and other works, and Railway Companies.' The works closed before the First World War and the site *(SY 938864)*, which lay close to Pike Brothers' clay depot, has since been reclaimed and built over.

The shore at Kimmeridge was indirectly associated with cement making. Two cement stone bands were quarried and mined from the lower part of the cliff between Cuddle and Clavell's Hard, but in this case the stone was shipped away to the Isle of Wight for the manufacture of 'Medina' hydraulic cement. It was taken for the construction of the breakwaters at Alderney and Cherbourg, but by 1886 was little used. The East Ledge stone band was said to be the most valued. Some collapsed adit levels with tramway rails protruding from the cliff may be part of this activity, rather than for the oil shale which was found higher up the cliff. Cement stone was also taken from Broad Bench on the west side of Kimmeridge Bay.

9

❧ BRICK MAKING ❧

Nature reserves and industry seem hardly compatible, but a small Suffolk-type brick kiln survives in the Dorset Wildlife Trust's reserve at Powerstock Common *(SY 542974)*. It is the very isolation of this site that has saved it. Although small, the Powerstock kiln is the best of the few preserved brick kilns in Dorset, with four iron firing doors intact and in position. It was built when suitable Fuller's Earth clay was discovered in a nearby cutting of the Bridport Railway in 1857. Drying sheds were also built and the kiln may have worked for twenty to thirty years. About 25,000 bricks were fired by up to 12 tons of coal. The upper part of the kiln has gone, but it was loaded and unloaded through two openings or 'wickets' which were sealed with clay and old bricks before firing started. The open top may have been covered with corrugated iron. Such a kiln could have made around 200,000 bricks a year, as well as tiles and field drains.

There have been around 170 brickyards in Dorset at various times in the past. Bricks for building in Dorset were becoming more common in the seventeenth century and by the 1700s small local brickyards were increasing in number and capacity. The

main period of activity was the half-century from about 1850, which was a time of railways and when large building developments were gathering pace around Poole and Bournemouth. Bricks and tiles were in great demand, but after a peak around the turn of the century a reduced industry continued until 1939 when there were still about 25 brick and tile makers in Dorset. The Second World War brought another decline, from which there was little recovery. The final gasp was in the late-1960s when most remaining yards could no longer compete against the increasing availability of other building materials or cheaper bricks manufactured far beyond the county. Plastic piping was to have a severe effect on the traditional earthenware pipes which were also made at brickyards. There were less than six brickyards in 1970, and the two at work today have survived by making a specialist product: hand-made bricks at Swanage and calcium silicate bricks at Beacon Hill near Corfe Mullen.

Like quarried stone, bricks were expensive to carry any great distance, so every available clay source was exploited. The Oxford, Kimmeridge and Bagshot beds were the most commonly used, with others including the Gault, Fuller's Earth and Wealden clays, in locations as widespread as Shaftesbury, Bridport and Swanage. The geological variations in these clay types produced fired bricks of distinctive colour and texture, sometimes deliberately sought, which can be recognised in buildings all over Dorset. For example, a harsh red from the Kimmeridge clay is seen in many nineteenth- and twentieth-century buildings at Gillingham, while bricks from the Reading beds at Broadmayne have a characteristic speckled effect caused by nodules of manganese oxide in the clay. These were widely used in Dorchester and Weymouth. Yellow and pale bricks were used to good effect for architectural decoration. Although bricks were their mainstay, many brickyards had sidelines in special bricks, floor and roof tiles, roof finials, chimney-pots, water and drainpipes or sanitary wares.

The brickyard was sited close to the source of clay. In a small local brickyard the clay was dug from the pit during the winter and allowed to weather in a heap. The pits were dug by hand but a steam excavator was recorded at the South Western Pottery, Parkstone, in 1922 and a multibucket excavator worked at Gillingham from 1937 until 1969. As the pit was extended or new

One of the four iron fire doors of a small Suffolk-type brick kiln preserved in the Powerstock Common nature reserve.

deposits were opened up further from the brick-yard, the clay was carried to the works on tramways worked first by horses and then small diesel or petrol locomotives from the early-twentieth century. The narrow-gauge line at Gillingham brickworks, for example, had a diesel locomotive in its final years.

The next stage was to mix (temper) the clay in a pug mill turned either by hand or by horse power. Originally, men would tread the clay with their feet. Summer was the time for making bricks by hand. After being rolled in sand a 'clot' of clay was thrown into a wooden mould and a man could produce up to 800 bricks a day and even more if he had an assistant. These 'green' bricks were dried in open air 'hacks' or long open-sided drying sheds. From the mid-nineteenth century steam power was used at the larger works to drive the mill and machines for producing extruded wire-cut bricks. Gillingham brickworks took power from a locally made steam engine from 1865 until 1937 when electricity took over. By about 1900 small oil or gas engines were being used in smaller brickyards.

Firing took place in intermittent or continuous types of kiln. Intermittent types were the updraught Suffolk kiln (as at Powerstock) and Scotch kiln (at Studland) or downdraught kiln (rectangular at Swanage and circular at Bourton). Loading and unloading was a laborious business by hand (today it is done with a fork-lift truck), and firing took about three days and as much time for the bricks to cool before they could be taken out. The larger Hoffmann kiln could be used continuously, with over 12 chambers being fired in rotation, with some chambers burning, others cooling, unloading or loading. Invented in 1867, only about a dozen of this type of kiln were ever built in Dorset, among the most recent being at Bothenhampton (Bridport) and Chickerell (Weymouth). A disadvantage of the Hoffmann kiln was that it needed a regular output to keep it going, so the intermittent kilns were better suited to the building demands of a small rural county.

While the brickyards were well distributed across Dorset, there were some areas with greater concentrations. Many brickyards were established in the Poole, Parkstone and Bournemouth area, where there was a good market on hand for building materials during the nineteenth and early-twentieth centuries. Even in 1826, C. & J. Greenwood's one-inch map of Dorset showed four brick kilns and one 'kiln' close to Poole. From the 1850s, several works were established to produce mainly tiles and earthenware pipes, such as at Kinson, Bourne Valley, Parkstone and on Brownsea Island. They are described in the following chapter on potteries.

A number of brickworks supplied the building needs of Weymouth when the resort town rapidly expanded in the nineteenth century. The first recorded brickyard was in 1794 and by the 1850s Putton Lane and Crook Hill at Chickerell were two important works using Oxford clay. These were the last to close, in 1965 and 1969. The former had two downdraught Scotch kilns and a Hoffmann kiln. The pit at Crook Hill was dug by hand until as late as 1958. Burning was economical because of a combustible material in the clay known as 'fiery' which could be used as a fuel. A continuous Hoffmann kiln was built here in about 1900 and was perhaps the oldest surviving example in Dorset until demolition in 1996. In its last year of working in 1969 this kiln was producing 70,000 bricks per week. G.H. Crickmay had the works in 1850, ownership later passing in the 1900s to Messrs Webb Major who had another brickyard at Broadmayne. At the time of closure Crook Hill and Putton Lane were owned by Mitchell & Son of Downton, Wiltshire. Brickyards at Broadmayne village dug clay from the Reading beds and sent their products 3 miles to Dorchester, where their distinctive speckled bricks can be seen in many houses. The last yard closed in 1940 but there were some remains until at least 1970.

There were at least seven brickyards in and around Bridport. The North Allington brickyard was recorded in 1797. David Biddlecombe, a farmer, worked a brickyard here from the 1850s and in 1881 many bricks were exported as far as New Zealand. The yard closed before the Second World War. The Bridport Terra Cotta, Brick, Tile, Pipe & Pottery Works exploited the Oxford clay at Bothenhampton from 1889 to 1952. A horizontal steam engine worked the pug mill and other machinery, as well as hauling tubs up to the moulding shed. Extruded wire-cut bricks were produced and fired in a continuous Hoffmann kiln. After closure the site became the town's rubbish tip.

There were at least 23 brickyards in and around the Blackmoor Vale in north Dorset where the Oxford, Kimmeridge and Gault clays were all exploited. In 1854, Louis Ruegg claimed the Kimmeridge clay made excellent drainpipes, and three works had recently opened near Shaftesbury. Further, 'Lord Rivers has opened clay pits at Okeford, and is expending large sums on this fundamental work.' The largest brickyard in the Vale was the works of the Gillingham Pottery, Brick & Tile Co. Ltd which operated from 1865 until 1969 and enjoyed the convenience of a siding at Gillingham Railway Station. The harsh reddish-orange bricks are a distinguishing feature of buildings in

THE

[Established 1866

Gillingham Pottery, Brick & Tile Co., Ltd.,

— MANUFACTURERS of every description of —

BRICK, TILE, PIPE
AND
POTTERY GOODS,

BRICKS—Building (Solid and Perforated), Pressed, Wire-cut.

BRICKS—Air, Angle, Arch, Dog-Tooth, Moulded, Ornamental, Cornice, Plinth, Red-pressed, Sills, Headers, Stretchers, Octagon.

BRICKS — Stable, Sewer and Channel Bricks.

PAVING BRICKS in various sizes.

COPINGS for Gables, Walls and Platforms.

Roofing and Garden Edging TILES of every description.

DRAIN PIPES from 2in. diameter up to 16in.

Chimney, Rhubarb, Seakale and Flower POTS in great variety.

FOR
ARCHITECTURAL
+ BUILDING
AND OTHER PURPOSES.

———o———

Garden Vases, Rustic Ferneries, Pots, &c., of all kinds.

SPECIALITY

Pressed Broseley Plain Roofing Tiles.

Glazed Stoneware Drain Pipes and Stourbridge Fire Bricks always in Stock.

Any kind of Clay Goods made to order.

Prices and Samples on application to

Mr. GEORGE HARRIS, Manager, GILLINGHAM, Dorset.

Advertisement for Gillingham brickworks, 1898.

Gillingham and the surrounding district, while roof tiles, ridges and finials are also of note. It is as well that something remains to be seen of the firm's efforts, for the brickyard site has vanished beneath an industrial estate. One flooded clay pit now provides a venue for local anglers. There were brickyards below Shaftesbury in the

Kimmeridge clay at Hawker's Hill and in the Gault clay at Long Cross, where a map of 1779 by James Upjohn clearly marked a 'brick kiln' and drying sheds. On the north Dorset border, there were two brickyards at Bourton (Kimmeridge clay) and another at Kington Magna (Oxford clay). In 1858 it was recorded that T. Hearne at Bagber Common and Mr Rowe at King's Stag were producing 200,000 bricks a year in addition to 200,000 and 20,000 tiles respectively.

Swanage is famed for its stone industry, so it is the more surprising to find a working brickyard there. Hand-made bricks and special shapes of higher value than common bricks are still manufactured at Godlingstone, just outside Swanage *(SY 020803)*. This small rural brickyard has been using Wealden clays from an adjacent pit since 1861, but the traditional methods of brick making are supported by modern processing equipment and kilns. Three downdraught kilns are gas-fired, and successors to earlier oil and coal firing.

Swanage brickworks, showing chimneys and kilns.

A downdraught kiln at Swanage brickworks, fired at the side by gas but previously by oil. Such kilns were originally fired by coal.

Surprisingly little remains of the once widespread brick-making industry. After closure many brick-yards were quickly demolished and their sites given over to industrial or housing estates, while some clay pits became landfill sites or amenities. Occasionally some structures remained for a few years before succumbing to the bulldozer, as at Crook Hill. The Brickfields Industrial Estate is the only memorial at Gillingham, as are place-names such as 'Brick Kiln Plantation' at East Stoke or 'Brickyard Lane' at Bourton. Other clues come from the bricks or other products impressed with their maker's name or initials. 'W' for the Westminster estate at Motcombe is common around Shaftesbury, while 'R. English, King Stagg' is a reminder of a small brickyard in the Blackmoor Vale. The collection of artefacts at the

Workmen and a circular downdraught kiln at Bourton in about 1930, where Andrew Harris was described as a brick and tile maker and drainpipe specialist.

GILLINGHAM MUSEUM

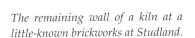

A brick manufactured by R. English at King's Stag in the Blackmoor Vale. The maker's name or initials moulded on one side of a brick often helps identify its source and how far it was transported.

Water Supply Museum at Sutton Poyntz includes some fine earthenware water pipes stamped 'R. Spencer. Sturminster Newton' within a fancy border decoration (see page 54).

There are, however, a few small historic kilns still standing. At the site of Bourton's brick, pipe and tile works there is a small circular downdraught kiln *(ST 772303)*, and a tunnel under the lane from the clay pit survives too. A small brickworks at Studland is believed to have worked from the 1890s until the early-twentieth century, and brick arches of a Scotch kiln have been conserved beside Wadmore Lane on the edge of Studland Heath *(SZ 030830)*. The little brick kiln at Powerstock Common opened this section.

The remaining wall of a kiln at a little-known brickworks at Studland.

Advertisement for the Kington Magna brickyard, 1889.

10

❧ TILES, PIPES AND POTS ❧

Poole Pottery became a familiar name in English decorated tablewares during the twentieth century. By coincidence, the shores of Poole Harbour saw the first organised pottery production back in the Roman period when Black Burnished wares were made from local clays to supply military establishments throughout Britain. The beginning of the pottery industry in Poole in modern times was in tiles and architectural wares, using ball clay, china clay, ground flint and feldspar. Although increasing tonnages of Purbeck ball clay had been exported to the Staffordshire potteries since the eighteenth century, there were few attempts to use this resource for a local industry. In fact it was not until the 1850s that there was a sudden flurry of activity around Poole with the establishment of works for making architectural wares, tiles and pipes. The railway, which arrived at Hamworthy in 1847, seems to have been the catalyst and entrepreneurs seized the new opportunities.

The Patent Architectural Pottery (*SZ 003904*) was opened at Hamworthy in 1854 by Thomas Ball, John Ridgeway, and Thomas and Frederick Sanders from Stoke-on-Trent, and after 1861 the Sanders brothers had complete control. It was an impressive works, with an engine house, decorated chimney, bottle kilns and other buildings associated with the 'many ingenious and elaborate processes.' Products included patent coloured and glazed bricks and architectural mouldings, and tessellated, mosaic, coloured and quarry floor tiles. Moulded coats of arms, flowers and fruits were also available, all clearly aimed at a high-class market. Raw materials were 'the superior Dorsetshire clay' from Purbeck and Wareham, with Cornish china clay. Clay from the Canford estate was used for plain quarry tiles. The Architectural Pottery was bought by Jesse Carter (see below) in 1895 to produce tiles. From the early days there was a railway siding to the pottery, which later became part of the power station site in 1949.

The South Western Pottery (*SZ 039908*) was established at Lower Parkstone by George Jennings in 1856 to manufacture his patent sanitary pipes and other stoneware goods. Jennings had previously owned a pottery in Lambeth and had been chief sanitary engineer to the Great Exhibition of 1851. He exhibited in Australia and America and won a silver medal at Paris in 1867. An advertisement of the period invited:

> *…Architects and Gentlemen carrying out Building or Draining operations … to examine the principle of Jennings' patent sewer pipes, when their great superiority over the ordinary Socket Pipe must at once be apparent.*

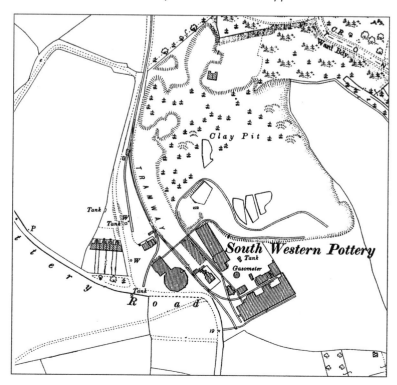

Jennings' South Western Pottery at Parkstone in 1900, from the Ordnance Survey 25-inch map.

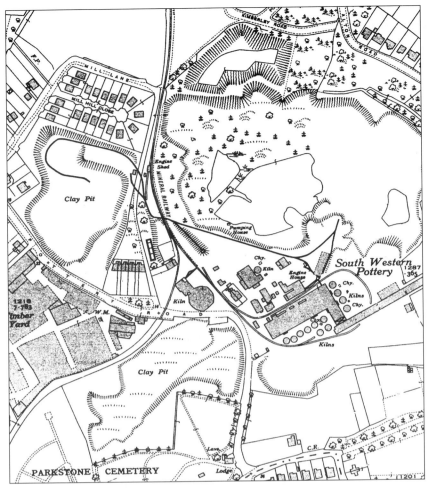

Jennings' South Western Pottery at Parkstone in 1937, from the Ordnance Survey 25-inch map. Note how the site has expanded since 1900.

The Kinson Pottery (*SZ 030926*) was also established in the 1850s and manufactured glazed sanitary stoneware, terracotta goods, bricks and field drainpipes. In 1907 there were 12 kilns, a boiler, engine house, drying sheds, stables and offices and 27 acres of clay were available on-site with three qualities in beds up to 40-feet thick. The Bourne Valley Pottery (*SZ 055921*) also made glazed stoneware, sewage and sanitary pipes, terracotta chimneys and vases, etc. There was a tramway connecting the pottery works to the mainline railway.

A rival pipe works was established almost by accident in 1855 on Branksea (Brownsea) Island out in Poole Harbour. Colonel Waugh planned to produce fine porcelain from clay deposits discovered on his island, but his high hopes were dashed when the clay proved only suitable for making less valuable glazed drainage pipes, sanitary wares and ornamental terracotta. Nevertheless, much

Terracotta wares were used in Bournemouth and are seen today in the eagles on the gateways to Poole Park. There was a brickworks here too, using a round Hoffmann continuous kiln. From about 1900 acid-resisting stoneware was manufactured and some was used at the Holton Heath cordite factory in the First World War. There was much expansion at the pottery and in 1930 Britain's first continuous salt-glazing tunnel kiln for pipes was built here.

A siding was laid from the main line at Parkstone Station in the 1890s and the pottery's own tank engines brought coal and returned with finished products. The last locomotive ceased work in 1963. A line also ran to Salterns Pier for shipping pipes. In addition, there were narrow-gauge lines to the clay pits. Steam engines supplied power for the machinery at the pottery and from 1930 a Bellis & Morcom vertical engine drove an electric generator for lighting and power for the tunnel kiln. The pottery closed suddenly at the beginning of 1967, allowing local industrial archaeologists to undertake a survey. Today, Pottery Road and South Western Crescent are reminders of the main pottery site that has been completely redeveloped for housing.

was invested in a works with two steam engines, a chimney, kilns, long drying sheds and other buildings on the southwest shore (*SZ 013875*). All were connected by a tramway to the Pottery Pier (New Pier) and the Seymour clay pits on the north side of the island. There were also brickworks, a smaller pottery, and a new village of workers' cottages at Maryland. Waugh was bankrupted in 1857 but the pottery works continued for another thirty years. In 1873 the island's new owner George Cavendish-Bentinck formed the Branksea Island Co. Ltd to manufacture sanitary pottery, terracotta work such as chimney-pots and ornamental figures, and by 1881 glazed sewer pipes had been used with success in Basingstoke, Portsmouth and the Isle of Wight. At its peak the pottery is said to have employed 300 but, despite the advantages of a shipping pier, the works closed in 1887. All that can be seen of this enterprise today are some overgrown foundations, and piles of broken pipes and bricks along the shoreline around Shard Point.

Meanwhile, James Walker had left his employment at the Architectural Pottery to build his own floor-tile works on Poole's East Quay in 1861.

Broken pipes banked on the shore at Shard Point are almost the only indication of a mid-nineteenth-century works on Brownsea Island.

This enterprise was unsuccessful and Jesse Carter bought the works in 1873, thus beginning the history of the Carter family's Poole Pottery *(SZ 012903)*. His sons Charles and Owen were brought into a partnership in 1881. They acquired the Architectural Pottery at Hamworthy in 1895 and most of their glazed and decorated wall and floor tiles and terracotta wares were produced there. In 1912 Carter & Co. also acquired the White Works at Hamworthy, where white tiles were made. This had been the Ultramarine Works from 1884 until about 1900. Meanwhile, at the East Quay pottery works, Owen Carter was experimenting and developing the decorative pottery which was to become the future of the firm. Painters and designers came to work at Poole. After the First World War, when the demand for tiles had declined, Charles Carter and his son Cyril were joined by the noted designer Harold Stabler and craft potter John Adams, forming Carter, Stabler & Adams Ltd to market the brightly coloured hand-painted wares for which Poole Pottery is so well known. The 1930s were fruitful years, turning also to tablewares, but expansion plans were thwarted by the Second World War, when only utility wares were made and tile making ceased. It was not until 1947 that the East Quay site was modernised to revive the trade. In 1964 the firm amalgamated with Pilkington Tiles of Manchester and continued to produce new lines, but Poole Pottery became independent again in 1992. Pottery making moved from the historic quay site when it was totally redeveloped for prestigious residences in 2002.

Outside Poole, the Sandford Pottery *(SY 927894)* was established near Wareham in 1860 with the intention of producing fine china using a work-

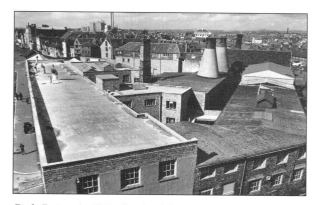

Poole Pottery in 1949, showing kilns and the confined nature of the triangular site near the quay. The new Poole Power Station is in the background, but fifty years later both sites have gone.

The newly redeveloped Poole Pottery on the quay in 1949, with a glimpse of the gasworks overhead coal crane beyond. Notice the rail tracks on the quay.

force of Staffordshire potters. As had happened on Brownsea Island, this was not to be, and the main products were bricks, chimney-pots, drainage pipes, garden edges and kitchen sinks. A tramway branch connected the works to the main railway. The pottery was in the hands of the Shaw family from 1895 until its closure in 1966, after which the derelict buildings and chimney remained a local landmark until demolition in 1979 to make way for a housing estate. The nearby Sibley craft pottery was established in 1920 using ball clay for its products which were fired in three kilns. The pottery was closed during the Second World War, and was then leased until 1959 by Branksome China, a firm started by a former manager of Poole Pottery.

Earthenware water pipe made by R. Spencer of Sturminster Newton, now preserved at the Sutton Poyntz Water Supply Museum.

Another aspect of the Dorset pottery industry has received deserved attention in recent years. It is remarkable that just a few miles from the major potteries at Poole there were small coarse-earthenware potteries still carrying on their activities in the old traditional ways. These were by far the most important rural potteries in Dorset and 40 production sites dating from the seventeenth century onwards have been identified in the vicinity of Alderholt, Crendell, Horton and Verwood. The range of everyday products included storage pots, bushel pans, cream pans, jugs and costrels (Dorset 'owls') and their collective term 'Verwood Wares' comes from the main centre at Verwood, which had 11 known sites. Decline was rapid in the early-twentieth century, with five Verwood sites closing between 1907 and 1914, but the Cross Roads Pottery carried on as the very last of the potteries until 1952. It was begun in 1817 and by the end of the century the potter Fred Fry was making an effort to diversify and compete against mass-produced wares from elsewhere. He introduced decorated and rustic pottery and lavender water vessels, while special reproduction classical pots had been made for Gen. Pitt-Rivers, the famous archaeologist of Rushmore on Cranborne Chase. The Cross Roads Pottery was sold in 1925 and restarted two years later by Horace Thorn with Mesheck Sims as manager. In its last years the pottery was run by Hubert Bailey assisted by Les Sims. About ten years after closure, the site was cleared to build a bungalow.

The Verwood pottery sites have been located by scatters of wasters or the occasional kiln mound. Local clay deposits were dug from pits on poorer common land and a few traces remain. The clay was first prepared by being trampled underfoot, rolled and wedged by hand until it was brought to a plastic state. The pots were all wheel-thrown. At Cross Roads there were two wheels, one driven by a hand-crank and the other worked with bicycle pedals, chain and cogs (the latest in modernisation!). Most of the pots were plain wares or had simple incised decorations. A lead glaze and trace minerals in the clay gave the pots their final colour when fired, and the addition of manganese gave a dark brown glaze. A typical kiln was lined with brick and was about 10-feet round and high. A surrounding mound of earth, clay and broken pots gave support and insulation, and provided a platform for loading and unloading the kiln from the top. The kilns were fired to a temperature of 1000°C, using wood, faggots and furze cut from the heath. Broken pots were thrown aside, and the rest were either sold locally or packed in straw or heather and carried for sale around the region by hawkers with a packhorse or wagon. One of the last hawkers, 'Pans' Brewer, worked into the 1930s travelling as far as Bridport, Sherborne, Salisbury, Warminster and Yeovil. In the end, this declining industry could not compete against outside products spreading into the region as the result of improved transport networks.

Verwood pottery workers in the early-twentieth century.
VERWOOD & DISTRICT POTTERIES TRUST

A variety of wares at the Verwood potteries. Note the cob-walled buildings.
VERWOOD & DISTRICT POTTERIES TRUST

The Verwood & District Potteries Trust was formed in 1985 when the last traces of the industry were fast disappearing. Seventeenth- and eighteenth-century sites have been excavated at Crendall and Horton, and a site scheduled as an ancient monument at Dewlands Common near Verwood is complete with its kiln mound, drying shed and a small cob building. Museums at Christchurch, Dorchester and Poole have examples of the Verwood wares in their collection.

11

✤ CORN MILLING ✤

Corn milling is an ancient industry and the use of water power in Dorset dates back to Saxon times. Domesday Book recorded some 277 mills in the county by 1086, proof indeed of their significance in the local economy. During the following millennium hundreds of watermills were located on streams and rivers in the deepest countryside or within towns and villages. Successful sites were refurbished many times so that most mill buildings today date from the eighteenth and nineteenth centuries.

From the early-nineteenth century onwards, cast iron was used for waterwheels, sluices and milling machinery. These and other technological improvements, including turbines, introduced in the wake of the Industrial Revolution enabled the mills to stave off outside competition for a while longer. By 1907, traditional corn milling by water was said to have given way to steam mills, with many of the watermills ruinous or 'totally disappeared'. This was not quite true but the decline was relentless and numbers slipped dramatically in the twentieth century. Millers listed in *Kelly's Directory* had fallen from 148 in 1855, to 120 in 1895, and halved to 61 in 1923. On the eve of the Second World War there were just 37 millers left, and many more had ceased work by the end of the conflict. Some mills continued until the 1960s or a little later, often relying on the milling of animal feed. Today, the only commercial water-powered corn mill is at Cann *(ST 872208)* near Shaftesbury, and even this mill is a rebuild after a fire in the 1950s. A number of old mills have been converted to houses, with some retaining their wheels. A few have been restored and opened to the public, notably at Alderholt, Christchurch (Place Mill), Lyme Regis, Mangerton, Shapwick (White Mill) and Sturminster Newton.

Alderholt Mill's iron waterwheel by Munden of Ringwood replaced an older internal wheel. The sluice at this mill is lowered to raise the water level to provide a working head for the wheel.

A typical corn or grist mill had three floors, with a bin floor at the top and the stones on the first floor. The internal or external wheelpit contained an undershot, breastshot or overshot wheel according to the head of water available. Power was transmitted from the wheel shaft (axle) by the pit wheel, wallower, upright shaft and great spur wheel to drive two or more millstones. Later millwork had cast-iron geared wheels with hard-

The twin mills at Mangerton near Bridport, showing the corn mill (left) and former flax and sawmill (right).

Pit wheel, wallower and great spur wheel, with upright shaft on an iron arch, Alderholt Mill.

wood cogs, but White Mill, near Shapwick, is of special interest as it has rare eighteenth-century wooden gearing. Other equipment could be worked, such as a hoist for raising grain sacks to the bin floor. Outside hoists were often given protection by a weather-boarded 'lucam', a feature seen on other industrial buildings such as breweries or warehouses. Elevators were used for moving grain within the mill.

Grain was ground between the closely set runner and bed stones, fed into the centre of the stones and discharged as meal at the outside. Millstones were around 3 feet 6 inches to 4 feet in diameter. Millstones of sandstone conglomerate from Somerset or South Wales were used but the 'peaks' of millstone grit from Derbyshire were more common. The best millstones were the French burr-stones, imported throughout the nineteenth century from the Paris basin. These hard millstones are easily recognised because they were made in segments and held with iron hoops. Composition millstones of emery and cement needed less dressing, but were best only for animal feeds.

The usual arrangement was to have two pairs of millstones and periodically one set would have to be laboriously dressed by hand. The heavy stones were mounted on a strong wooden hurst frame that was integral to the mill. Later hurst frames were made of cast iron and Cann Mill, for example, has hursts made by Taskers of Andover and Ruston & Proctor of Lincoln. After grinding, the meal was sifted to separate the broken husks or bran, using rotating machines, such as a bolter which forced fine flour out through a cloth sleeve, or a wire machine which separated different grades of flour at the same time.

Water turbines became increasingly popular from the last quarter of the nineteenth century, being more efficient and requiring little maintenance. Turbines could dispense with heavy gearing by using pulleys and belts instead. Their size was well suited to the small rural corn mills and several were installed as a way of competing against the new steam mills. The main supplier from the 1880s was Joseph J. Armfield of Ringwood who installed at least 31 turbines in corn mills and other Dorset sites during 1887–1923. The 'British Empire' turbine was the most popular and came in a variety of sizes. There are examples of other turbines by Hick Hargreaves & Co. of Bolton at West Mill, Bridport, C. Cadle of Dublin at Purn's Mill at Gillingham, and G. Gilkes of Kendal at Bryanston Home Farm.

A French burr-stone, showing the typical construction in segments. This one is at Cann Mill near Shaftesbury.

Joseph J. Armfield of Ringwood installed many turbines in Dorset. This drawing shows the 20-inch double 'British Empire' turbine of about 1900.

The location of corn and farm mills along the smallest of streams illustrates the importance of water power in rural Dorset. Water was taken direct from a weir on a river, or by a leat from a weir further upstream. Mills on smaller streams or close to a spring had a millpond to conserve water for a day's working while also increasing the head; the mills at Cann and Barfoot Farm near Shaftesbury are good examples. Occasionally, water came from more than one supply, and the large wheel at Upwey Mill *(SY 663851)* had two

Upwey Mill was built in 1802 when it is said to have provided flour for the military during the Napoleonic Wars. Handsomely built in Portland stone, it has a large iron waterwheel under the arched opening.

sources. In all cases, the miller controlled the water flow by hatches or sluices.

The rural mills were small and therefore numerous. In west Dorset, the River Brit and its tributaries provided power for mills at Beaminster, Bridport, Netherbury, Stoke Abbott, Loders and Mangerton, this last being a mill in working order and open to the public *(SY 490957)*. There were mills on the tributaries of the Yeo at Chetnole, Holt and Halstock, and on the upper reaches of the Axe around Mosterton. There were places with greater concentrations, such as Sydling Water which had eight waterwheels (mostly on farms) in 5 miles, or the parallel River Cerne with eight mills in 4 miles, at Cerne Abbas, Nether Cerne, Godmanstone and Forston. Both streams are tributaries of the River Frome which also had corn mills, but there was always competition here with the water meadow systems. The finest surviving mill on this river is at Maiden Newton *(SY 596977)*, where an external 16-feet diameter by 10-feet wide breastshot waterwheel by Winter & Hossey of Dorchester was a replacement for two smaller internal wheels.

This large wheel at Maiden Newton measures 16-feet diameter and 10-feet wide and was made by Winter & Hossey of Dorchester.

The upper course of the River Stour and its tributaries draining the Blackmoor Vale basin offer much of interest with around 40 water-powered sites. There were at least 16 corn mills along the Stour between Bourton and Blandford, of which only four have disappeared. The youthful Stour enters Dorset at Bourton, where one of three waterwheels at the Maggs' flax and iron works drove a grist mill. Downstream, Silton Mill, Waterloo Mill and Eccliffe Mill have become houses, but the derelict Highbridge Mill *(ST 790229)* at East Stour has a turbine beside the wheelpit and Stour Provost Mill *(ST 791215)* contains one of E.S. Hindley's wheels, dated 1889. The next two mills, at Marnhull and Fifehead, have gone. West Mill *(ST 756192)* at Stalbridge has a Hindley wheel of 1893 that was replaced by a 40hp Ruston & Hornsby oil engine when the

Stour was diverted in 1943 to avert flooding at the Henstridge airfield. The former river loop, where the mill stands, now takes water from the tributary River Cale.

King's Mill *(ST 766172)* is an early-nineteenth-century stone building below Marnhull. It last worked in 1935 and the weir and undershot wheel are derelict, although the machinery inside was

King's Mill on the River Stour at Marnhull.

West Mill at Stalbridge, where animal feeds are processed, has a disused iron wheel by Hindley of Bourton, and an oil engine.

This Ruston & Hornsby oil engine was installed during the Second World War when the Stour was diverted away from West Mill, Stalbridge.

restored in 1993. Cut Mill *(ST 776165)* is on a large weir at Hinton St Mary and has been rebuilt at least three times. Sturminster Newton Mill *(ST 782135)* is a well-known landmark beside a prominent weir. The oldest part of the mill dates from 1648, with an eighteenth-century extension. Milling ceased in 1969, but the mill was restored in 1981 and opened to the public. A belt and layshafts drive the millstones, crushers, winnower and sack hoists, as well as two hammer mills installed in about 1947. Joseph Armfield replaced two internal waterwheels with a 45-inch diameter British Empire turbine in 1904. He was busy in this neighbourhood, fitting out Cut Mill in 1910 with milling machinery and new hatches, and supplying a turbine in 1907 to the next mill downstream at Fiddleford *(ST 801136)*. Set in a wall of the latter is a curious inscription of 1566 which may record a rebuilding during the time of miller Thomas White.

Bere Marsh Mill at Shillingstone ceased work in 1923 and has since been demolished. Durweston Mill *(ST 859089)* is a substantial building, converted to housing, but Whitecliff Mill ('Whitley Mill' on Isaac Taylor's 1765 map), upstream from Blandford Forum, has long since gone.

Of the Stour's tributaries, the fast-flowing upper reaches of the Stirchel Brook south of Shaftesbury had five corn mills within a mile in the nineteenth century, at Melbury Abbas (Barfoot Farm), Spragg's Mill, Cann Mill, French Mill and Gears Mill. A second stream springing from the chalk, the Fontmell Brook, had at least seven mills, including Higher Mill, Piper's Mill, Hurdle's Mill, Pegg's Farm and Farrington Mill. Other tributaries, the Shreen Water, Caundle Brook, Lydden, Divelish and Iwerne rivers, powered at least 11 more mills or farm wheels.

Cut Mill and its weir on the River Stour at Hinton St Mary. Extensions to the mill are clearly seen.

Sturminster Newton Mill is powered by an Armfield turbine and is open to the public.

The Stour has two notable mills below Blandford. White Mill (*ST 958006*) was restored in 1994 by the National Trust and contains wooden mill gearing of the 1770s. This large brick mill was rebuilt in 1776, after it had become a part of the Kingston Lacy estate, and two internal undershot waterwheels drove millstones, sack hoists and flour cleaners. Throop Mill (*SZ 113958*) was rebuilt in about 1900 when a 60-inch Armfield turbine was installed to drive four roller mills, flour dressers and elevators. Parsons & Sons took over in 1926 and used the mill to supply their bakeries. Heygates of Northampton last worked the mill from 1957 until 1972 when the water supply was lost to a flood-relief scheme. Canford Mill below Wimborne was completely destroyed in a fire on New Year's Day 1894. This large mill had been leased by W.H. Yeatman & Sons Ltd in 1871 and improved over the years to become 'one of the best' mills on the river, with turbines and modern equipment. The mill blaze destroyed 500 sacks of flour, but all was insured. Yeatman's moved to the new Victoria Steam Flour Mills at Poole which worked until the 1930s.

The River Stour at Throop Mill.

Gillingham Town Mill is seen still at work in about 1960, with G.B. Matthews & Co.'s lorry alongside.

Town Mill, Lyme Regis, in about 1880. This mill in the heart of the town has been restored to working order.

COURTESY H.G. FLAMBERT AND LYME REGIS TOWN MILL TRUST

Many villages had mills, as still seen at Corfe Castle, Litton Cheney, Charminster, Godmanstone or Sutton Poyntz. The towns of Bridport, Dorchester, Gillingham, Lyme Regis, Wareham and Wimborne Minster could support one or more mills, which became increasingly important as their populations rose in the nineteenth century. The Town Mill at Lyme Regis *(SY 342922)* had two overshot water-wheels, the last being an internal one made in 1888 by Samson of Bridport. After closing in the late-1920s, the mill was used for a time for electricity generation, but it has been fully restored and a waterwheel reinstated in a development incorporating a gallery and craft workshops.

West Mill at Bridport is a fine example of a late-nineteenth-century mill containing a turbine.

In Bridport, West Mill (SY 463930) was also a bolling mill for the flax industry, but had returned to just corn milling when occupied in 1864–75 by Henry Hansford. It was rebuilt in 1878–80 as the neat brick building seen today and a turbine manufactured by Hick Hargreaves & Co. of Bolton was installed to work three pairs of millstones. John Fowler was miller from at least 1895 until 1939. The derelict West Mill was converted to an office in the 1980s, preserving the turbine, a winnower and grain elevators inside. South Mill (SY 467924) on the River Asker served Bothenhampton. This four-storey mill is now surrounded by a council depot, with its watercourse blocked, although the weir and hatches survive.

The introduction of roller milling in 1862 dealt a severe blow to traditional stone milling. Most of Dorset's traditional watermills were unable to invest and continued to use stones and the old technology. Not only did roller mills process larger quantities of grain, but steam power released milling from remote river sites. Large steam roller mills were built in the ports, where grain was imported, and larger centres of population which were the main markets for flour. At Poole Quay, a large steam mill was built in 1864 by George & Thomas Belbin, and W.H. Yeatman & Sons built the Victoria Steam Flour Mill in the 1890s. They worked at least until the 1920s and 30s. Such locations also benefited from access to

The hatches are seen raised at the sluice of South Mill, Bridport.

railways for moving grain and flour products. The advent of motor lorries in the early-twentieth century, with their greater range, was another factor in the decline of small rural mills.

At Dorchester, Fordington Mill *(SY 700906)* was a large town mill fitted out with modern equipment in the late-Victorian period. There had been mills on this site ever since Domesday, and finally Arthur J. Legg spent a large sum turning it into a steam roller mill considered to be 'one of the most perfect in the country'. The *Dorset County Chronicle* reported the opening day in 1892 and described the workings in some detail. The four-storey mill was powered by a 100hp compound tandem condensing engine with a Lancashire boiler, manufactured by Thomas Robinson & Son Ltd of Rochdale. Miss May Brown officially named the engine 'May', and the high- and low-pressure cylinders 'Pioneer' and 'Industry'.

Robinsons also supplied the very latest in milling equipment. Wheat from the large grain silos was first blended and cleaned, before milling by machinery that was 'a marvel of ingenuity'. There were six double roller mills on the first floor of the mill, two for breaking the wheat down and cleaning the bran, and four for flouring the middlings, while a magnetic separator removed nails and other metal objects. The second floor had four 'Koh-i-noor' purifiers, a rotary scalper and two separating sieve purifiers, while the third floor had flour dressers, two double rotary scalpers and a separating sieve purifier. The older part of the mill was retained for milling animal feed, where a 24-inch 'Little Giant' turbine drove three pairs of stones.

This was a brave attempt to compete with the larger port-based mills, and wheat was carried here from local farms, with imported grain coming by rail from Bristol and London. The Dorchester Roller Flour Mills Co. Ltd was here by 1911, but Fordington Mill was closed and converted to housing in 1940, with later extensions in 1986. A date stone 'AIL 1891' on the east gable records Legg's rebuilding. Elsewhere, a carved stone is preserved from an earlier mill belonging to William Churchill, with the initials WC and date 1590. This carving once also bore the motto 'Do well to all men', which Legg used as his trademark.

Steam supplemented water power at some other mills, including Walford Mill *(SU 009007)* at Wimborne, now an arts centre. This originally had two undershot waterwheels, but a steam engine was later installed, of which the chimney survives. Not far away, White Mill on the Stour is believed to have had a small steam engine in the late-nineteenth century. Gas or oil engines were installed in a few mills, as described above at West Mill, Stalbridge.

Dorset's streams were not the only source of power for corn milling, for the county had perhaps 41 windmill sites. They stood on high ground or near the coast where they were well placed to catch the wind. The first recorded windmill was at Buckhorn Weston in 1267 and most information is found in manorial records or place-name evidence. All that remain are two stone towers on Portland, and a few windmill mounds. A small tower mill based on a Portuguese design was erected on the roof of Cann Mill as late as 1971.

The earliest types were wooden post-mills, built around a central post supported by quarterbars and crosstrees anchored in a mound. These have long since gone, save the mound, and evidence is found in documents and early maps. Isaac Taylor's Map of Dorset, 1765, shows a windmill on Hoggen Down at Milton Abbas, and 'Windmill Point' at Baiter Point, Poole, probably a post-mill of sixteenth-century origin. Taylor also shows 'Old Windmill' just north of Langton Matravers where there is now a low hill called 'Windmill Knap' *(SZ 006801)*. 'Cashmore Mill' is marked on the Ordnance Survey one-inch map of 1811 at Gussage St Michael, but only the arable 'Windmill Field' appears on the Tithe Map of 1841. Place names on modern Ordnance Survey maps include 'Windmill Hill' *(ST 729107)* near King's Stag and 'Windmill Hill' *(ST 623216)* near Sandford Orcas, while 'Windmill Barrow' *(SY 937977)* is indeed a mound at Windmill Barrow Farm, Lytchett Matravers.

Tower mills were built from the early-seventeenth century. These had a solid stone tower with a cap for turning the sails into the wind. The four sails were fitted on stocks attached to a windshaft bearing a large brake wheel to engage with a wallower and upright shaft. Machinery inside the mill was identical to a watermill except that the power to the millstones was transmitted from above.

The two windmill towers at Easton, Portland, in 1977.

Two stone windmill towers stand close together at Easton on Portland, which is remarkable for any county. They may date from the seventeenth century, as two windmills are shown here on maps of 1626 and 1710. Taylor marked them in 1765 and they appear on all subsequent maps. These mills were in an ideal spot on the windswept plateau, where they serviced the needs of an island with no streams. They also remind us that corn was grown in Portland's open fields long before quarrying became the dominant industry. Both towers have good stonework and are of similar dimensions, about 23-feet high and 12-feet internal diameter, but the south mill *(SY 692713)* may have been rebuilt since it tapers near the top. The north mill *(SY 691714)* was the last of the pair to work in the 1890s, when Edward and Robert Pearce were recorded as millers. The windshaft and a sail stock have been preserved at the Portland Museum.

Portland's south windmill tower is perilously close to the edge of a deep quarry.

12

❧ BEER ❧

Dorset has long been famous for its beers and by the early-eighteenth century Dorchester was deemed to brew the finest beer in England with a reputation as far away as London. Thomas Hardy was to write later of 'Casterbridge strong beer' in *The Trumpet Major*:

The masses worshipped it, the minor gentry loved it more than wine, and by the most illustrious county families it was not despised. Anybody brought up for being drunk and disorderly in the streets of its natal borough, had only to prove that he was a stranger to the place and its liquor to be honourably dismissed by the magistrates, as one overtaken in a fault that no man could guard against who entered the town unawares.

Most village inns had a small brewhouse at the back for their own purposes, although occasionally beer was carried further afield. Large mansions had brewhouses too, such as Smedmore House, Kimmeridge. The nineteenth century saw the building of small breweries in villages and towns, with capacity to serve a wider district. Much larger architect-designed breweries appeared in the second half of the century as transport facilities improved. The twentieth century was a period of consolidation when the large brewers took every opportunity to buy out and close their smaller neighbours while keeping the tied houses as outlets for their own beers. In 1950 there were still nine working breweries, at Blandford (two), Bridport, Dorchester, Gillingham, Milton Abbas, Sherborne and Weymouth (two). There are three independent breweries at work in the county today, at Blandford, Bridport and Dorchester.

Victorian breweries are among the most distinctive and handsome of all industrial buildings. Although the typical processes are relatively simple, successful brewing depends on the skill and experience of the brewer as well as the type and quality of raw materials. Malt barley, which gives beer its character, is passed through roller mills to crack the husks and mixed with hot water (liquor) in the mash tun where soluble starch is converted to malt sugar. After perhaps two hours of mashing, with revolving rakes, the porridge-like mixture is washed out with a hot-water spray and the sugary liquid (wort) drains through slotted base plates into the copper. Here the wort is mixed with sugar and hops. Different varieties of hops

give the beer its bitter flavour and aroma, while also sterilising the wort and giving the beer its keeping quality. After boiling in the copper, the wort passes through the hop back where spent hops are filtered out, and then it is cooled to room temperature by passing through a heat exchanger, and run into fermenting vessels.

Round fermentation vessels at Palmers' Old Brewery, Bridport.

This is where the brewer adds yeast of a particular strain to change the malt sugar to alcohol and carbon dioxide. Fermentation takes about four days, depending on the temperature, and the beer is then settled in tanks in the conditioning room. Draught beer is run down by gravity to the racking cellar for filling casks. Beer for bottling has further fermentation before cooling in the 'cold room'.

Little is wasted. Spent grains from the mash tun and hops from the copper are sold to farmers as cattle feed. The yeasty head is skimmed off the top of the fermenting brew and passed through a yeast press, part being kept for future brews and the surplus sold as animal feed. Energy is saved by using the hot water from the heat exchanger for new brewing liquor.

Most Victorian breweries had their own well to provide a guaranteed water supply of consistent quality for brewing liquor. Artesian wells at the Blandford and Fontmell breweries were sunk to 150 feet, but the well and bore at Dorchester was reported to be 586-feet deep in 1881. The record depth was at Wyke Brewery, Gillingham, where a borehole of 898 feet was only partly successful and was disused by 1926. By the late-nineteenth century a busy brewery would also have a cooperage for making and repairing barrels, a washing plant, bottling plant and a transport department with stables and drays.

Charles Hall established a brewery at Lower Ansty in 1777, and by the turn of the century had gained a lucrative contract to supply beer to the military camps in the Weymouth area during the invasion scare of the Napoleonic Wars. In 1847 his son Robert joined G.E.I. Woodhouse in partnership. Ever since Robert died eleven years later, the Woodhouse family remained in full control of the firm of Hall & Woodhouse. Although successful, the Ansty Brewery was small and remote, so a move was made to Blandford St Mary when John Hector's brewery was bought in 1883. A new large Blandford Brewery was built alongside at a cost of £28,000. It was almost completed when the old brewery burnt down accidentally in August 1900, so the Ansty Brewery was briefly brought back into operation. Malting continued at the old Ansty site until about 1940, and a malthouse has since become the village hall (ST 764032).

In 1902 Hall & Woodhouse Ltd were described as 'brewers, maltsters, beer bottlers, hop merchants, importers and bonders of wines and spirits, and aerated water manufacturers'. Since 1950, the brewery has expanded into the off-licence business and soft drinks trade, and now lager brewing and a modern canning production line ensure the success of this long-established firm. Although new buildings have been added, the Blandford Brewery (ST 886058) is still a distinctive late-Victorian tower brewery, in brick with adjoining maltings and a separate office building. Two small horizontal steam engines are preserved inside the brewery. The most complete was built in 1899 by Gimson of Leicester to work mash tuns and hoist malt sacks. The second is a Ruston & Proctor engine of c.1908 and was brought here after Hall & Woodhouse took over the Wyke Brewery at Gillingham in 1963.

Brewing in Dorchester is closely associated with Eldridge Pope & Co. Charles and Sarah Eldridge ran the Green Dragon in Durngate Street from their marriage in 1829, enlarged the brewery behind in 1837 and also briefly took on the Antelope Hotel from 1833–35. After Charles died in 1846, his wife took brewer Alfred Mason into partnership and by 1851 the Dragon Brewery was rivalling the Phoenix Brewery in the town, both employing about 12 persons. Sarah died in 1856 and her son-in-law John Tizard took over her share. The business expanded and when Mason retired in 1870 they had two breweries and seven malthouses, with three hotels and 26 pubs from Weymouth to Portsmouth. Edwin Pope now became a partner and his family bought the remaining share after Tizard died in 1873.

The brothers Edwin and Alfred Pope were in full control of Eldridge Pope & Co. in 1881 when they opened the large Dorchester Brewery (SY 692901) at a cost of £40,000. This was the work of the architect G.R. Crickmay of Weymouth, who also designed two maltings and a brewery at Weymouth. At the time of its opening the brewery was described as:

Blandford Brewery (left, background) with the large maltings on the right.

... a noble and imposing pile in a very ornate style of architecture ... the lofty and elegant chimney forming a conspicuous landmark for miles around. The premises constitute probably the finest pile of buildings devoted to industrial purposes in the South of England.

The site in Weymouth Avenue, just outside the heart of the old town, was a good choice, with sidings from the adjacent London & South Western Railway. This opened up potential markets along the railway route and the firm acquired tied houses in places such as Poole, Bournemouth, Southampton, Winchester and Portsmouth, and eventually as far as London. In 1890 three trains a day were arriving with raw materials and empties and leaving laden with barrels of beer.

Detail of polychrome brickwork on the Dorchester Brewery's bonded warehouse on Weymouth Avenue. The shield has the initials of Eldridge Pope & Co.

The Dorchester Brewery of 1880 was rebuilt after a fire in the 1920s. It is now known as the Thomas Hardy Brewery.

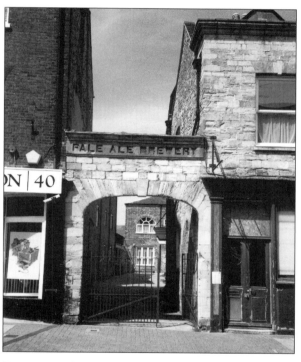

Entrance to the old Pale Ale Brewery in High East Street, Dorchester.

The complex included the main brewhouse in Broadmayne brick and Portland stone, a tall chimney, maltings (with a beer store beneath), offices and manager's residence, stables and sheds for vans and drays, and a cooperage. The stylish architecture was continued in the bonded warehouse alongside Weymouth Avenue. A devastating fire in November 1922 necessitated rebuilding, with the opportunity to install the latest equipment for the first new brew in February 1925. The old sidings have now gone and, despite alterations, the renamed Thomas Hardy Brewery contains much of original interest. In the heart of the town, Eldridge

& Mason's Green Dragon Brewery and Pale Ale Brewery were closed in 1883 after the new Dorchester Brewery opened, but 'Pale Ale Brewery' is still carved in stone above the entrance in High East Street *(SY 694908)*.

The Old Brewery *(SY 465921)* in West Bay Road, Bridport, is the smallest of the three working breweries in Dorset and has been owned by J.C. & R.H. Palmer since 1896. It was formerly the West Bay Brewery, founded in the eighteenth century and run by Job Legg since 1865. The oldest part is said to date from 1797 and has two thatched gabled roofs, each with a stone finial in the shape of a barrel. Alongside the River Brit at the rear of the brewery is a low breastshot waterwheel (19 feet by 5 feet) made of iron by Thomas Helyear of Bridport in 1879. This worked two pumps for

drawing water from the brewery's well. A small steam engine, by Brown & May of Devizes in Wiltshire, is preserved inside the brewery. A second brewery in Bridport was founded by Joseph Gundry in 1794. Job Legg was here from about 1820 until 1865 when he took his brewing to the West Bay Brewery described above. The stone buildings of the Bridport Brewery (SY 464927) survive in Gundry Lane, where they were used in later years as a bonded store.

Hope Square in Weymouth was the site of early brewing long before a brewery was established in the 1750s. J.A. Devenish took over in 1823 and William Devenish was here seven years later. The family firm was granted the first of several royal warrants in 1872 after supplying the Prince of Wales with beer. Two breweries in Cornwall were acquired in the 1920s, followed by the Redruth Brewery in 1934.

The Old Brewery at Bridport is said to be the only thatched brewery in Europe. The finials on the gables are stone beer barrels.

The iron waterwheel alongside the River Brit makes the Old Brewery one of the most interesting breweries in the South of England.

Meanwhile, a second brewery had been founded by the Groves family in 1840, growing into the large Hope Brewery of John Groves & Son. Both firms had expanded before they eventually merged in 1960.

The stylish brick façade of Weymouth Brewery, dated 1904. The site has been redeveloped as the Brewers Quay visitor attraction but the exterior remains little changed.

Initialled date stone seen on John Groves' Brewery.

Rear of the Weymouth Brewery, with a chimney base of 1869. The left-hand block with arched windows was added by John Groves in 1879.

Although the breweries of J.A. Devenish and John Groves at Weymouth have been closed since 1986, the whole site *(SY 681785)* remains a remarkable industrial landmark. The Brewers Quay attraction has been established behind an impressive brick frontage of 1904 (designed by Crickmay), with shops, restaurants, an exhibition and the Weymouth Museum. Two restored brewery steam engines are on display, the oldest manufactured by Barrett, Exall & Andrews of Reading in about 1851, and the other by E.S. Hindley & Sons of Bourton about forty years later. Cooperages, stabling and bottle stores are part of the site, as are the four malthouses described below.

On the outskirts of Gillingham, the Wyke Brewery *(ST 796266)* was rebuilt in the 1880s for the Matthews family, who ran it until 1963 when it was acquired and closed by rivals Hall & Woodhouse. The redundant premises were kept on for a while as a depot and bottling store, but were converted to flats after 1986. Although the rear has been altered, the main stone façade survives with twin towers for water tanks, and its Italianate design still speaks of Victorian optimism. Across the road is the stable block with G.B. Matthews' initials dated 1884 over the archway.

Wyke Brewery at Gillingham is seen here in 1985 before conversion to flats.

A few miles away across the Blackmoor Vale, the tall brewhouse of the Marnhull Brewery *(ST 780182)* is a landmark at Walton Elm, despite having long been converted into flats with a gabled roof. The brewery had been started by Thomas Burt in 1821, passed to Jennings & Baker and Styring, White & Co., until it was bought out by Eldridge Pope in 1913. After retaining the tied houses, they finally sold the Marnhull Brewery to Hall & Woodhouse in 1935. Just a field away was the Poplar Elm Brewery, now Hingarston House.

The Crown Brewery *(ST 867169)* in the centre of Fontmell Magna is a

The old Marnhull Brewery is a distinctive building seen across the fields at Walton Elm.

The Crown Brewery and brewer's house, Fontmell Magna. The brewery was rebuilt in 1876 by George Frederick Applin Flower, whose initials are carved with the date over a doorway.

good example of a small country brewery, built in brick with slate roofs. It was powered by a 20hp horizontal steam engine, and its industrial origins are confirmed by a covered hoist on the front wall and an iron roof tank made by H. Pontifex & Sons of King's Cross. It dates from a rebuilding in 1876 by George Frederick Applin Flower, whose sons continued as Flower Brothers until the brewery was sold to A. & T. Sibeth in 1898. The Fontmell brewery was closed soon afterwards in 1904, and its 21 pubs were sold off to eight other breweries, namely Hall & Woodhouse, Eldridge Pope, Matthews (Gillingham), Dolphin Brewery (Poole), Dorsetshire Brewery, Woolmington Bros (Sherborne), and Folliotts and Gibbs Mew of Salisbury.

Despite the brewery's short life, it was the scene of important innovations, as described by Alfred Barnard on a winter visit in 1890. The Flower Brothers, in partnership with R.J. Cousins, established the Springhead Works in the old Higher Mill where they invented and manufactured brewing equipment. These included a patent dry-hopping machine and a cask-washing machine that was worked by a waterwheel at the brewery. There was a pale ale cellar beneath the engineers' shop at Springhead, and the brewery stables and dray sheds were here too.

The influence of John Groves spread out from Weymouth in 1905 when the small village brewery at Sydling St Nicholas was bought out. This brewery of 1842 was powered by a waterwheel which remained until it was scrapped during a house conversion in the 1960s. Groves also took over and closed Wimborne's Julian Brewery in 1915. This brewery had been built in 1876 by George Habgood and the old brewhouse is still behind the adjacent Pudding and Pye public house (*SU 007000*). An earlier brewery here at the Three Lions was run by Joseph Piddle (not the best name for a brewer!) in 1848. The Town Brewery at Wimborne was closed by Hall & Woodhouse in 1937.

No brewery has survived in the Poole and Bournemouth area, all having been taken over and closed by outsiders. In 1925 Strong & Co. of Romsey bought the Bournemouth Brewery, retaining the premises in Holdenhurst Road as a depot to gain a foothold in southeast Dorset. They did the same to the Dolphin Brewery in Market Street, Poole, in the following year, while the Christchurch Steam Brewery lasted until 1934. Meanwhile, Styring & Co.'s Poole Brewery in Towngate Street, in which George Pope was already a partner, was taken over and closed by Eldridge Pope & Co. in 1899, although they continued to use its malthouse for some time into the new century. Indeed, malting was once an important side of the brewer's business.

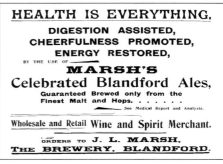

Advertisement for Marsh's Blandford Ales, 1903.

13

❧ MALT ❦

Malt for brewing was selected from the finest local barley and such was its reputation that barley malt was exported by sea from Dorset to Portsmouth and London in 1812. Welsh coal was used for kilning in 1793 when 10–12,000 bushels of malt were produced, about 10–14 bushels making a hogshead of 63 gallons of strong beer. Cerne Abbas, Blandford, Dorchester and Shaftesbury all traded in malt. Until the building of large maltings in towns and at breweries during the nineteenth century, there were numerous small village malthouses, such as at Fontmell Magna or Winterborne Stickland. Marnhull had five malthouses, while Cerne Abbas was also noted for its maltings until the 1820s. The usual arrangement of a floor malting was to have storage for the incoming barley at one end of the main malting floors and the kiln at the far end. Further storage was necessary for the malted barley. After selecting the finest barley grain, it was first 'steeped' in a water cistern. Until a malt tax was repealed in 1880, the steeped grain was next 'couched' to calculate the excise duty. This damp grain was then spread on the malting floor where it was allowed to germinate to render the starch solu-ble in water and release enzymes for converting it to sugar. The grain on the floor was raked, turned and watered periodically to ensure even germination. The skill of the maltster was to recognise the critical point to stop germination, when small shoots and rootlets had appeared. This green malt was next kilned to give it colour and flavour and then stored to mature and bagged. Nothing was wasted, as the dried rootlets and shoots were sold for animal feed.

The old malthouse at Nottington near Weymouth dates from 1834.

Charles Hall began a brewery at Ansty in 1777 but after Hall & Woodhouse moved to a new brewery at Blandford, malting continued at Ansty. At the time of this photograph, horses were the only means of transport from this isolated brewery.

HALL & WOODHOUSE

At Nottington (SY 661826) near Weymouth, a stone-built malthouse of three storeys was converted to housing in the 1970s but can be recognised by a cowl in the roof. A stone inscribed 'GNS 1834' suggests it dates from a time when maltings were beginning to become more than just a small village affair.

One of Dorset's best surviving industrial complexes is around the Brewers Quay development in Hope Square, Weymouth. In addition to the Devenish and Groves breweries, there are four notable floor maltings, three in very close proximity. No.1 Malthouse is of Portland stone and dates from before 1864. It has an L-shaped plan, with the barley store at right angles. This is the same arrangement seen in No.2 Malthouse which was designed for Messrs Devenish by the Weymouth architect G.R. Crickmay in 1861. No.4 Malthouse (SY 681785) was Crickmay's grandest design, immediately opposite the brewery, built for John Groves & Son in 1889. It is multi-storey, using polychrome brickwork and reinforced concrete floors. No.3 Malthouse dates from after 1864 and has a vernacular style in rough Portland stone like No.1. Half has been destroyed, but enough remains to recognise it as a malting. Despite low ceilings and small windows these floor maltings have been successfully converted to housing, and their external features remain largely intact.

A brewery landscape at Weymouth. The large floor malting to the right of the brewery is one of four nearby.

Weymouth's No.2 Malthouse was designed for Devenish by the local architect G.R. Crickmay in 1861. Although converted to housing, the two kilns are still recognisable with the barley warehouse at the far end and the malting floors between.

The No.4 Malthouse at Weymouth was built in 1889 for John Groves & Son to the design of local architect Crickmay, with a most impressive barley and malt store to the right. Now converted to flats, the name Groves is still visible on the kiln wall.

Twin kilns of the No.1 Malthouse, Weymouth.

The former maltings at Blandford Brewery were built as part of the original complex in 1900.

From the later-nineteenth century, brewers found it expedient to have their own malting floors on-site and, although no longer in use, they are still identifiable at Dorchester, Blandford and Bridport. In the 1870s Edwin Pope built the Town Maltings just north of South Walk in Dorchester. It was over 100-feet long with four storeys between malt stores at one end and a double kiln at the other. The lowest floor could store over 2000 barrels of beer. After demolition the site became a car park *(ST 694905)*, but the larger maltings at Dorchester Brewery are still there although not in use. There were two kilns and four storeys with 30 windows with ventilating shutters. The two malt floors measured 127 by 48 feet, with a barley loft in the upper floor and a beer store in the basement, dug from the chalk and connected by a long tunnel from the brewery. Part of the Old Brewery site at Bridport includes a floor malting with a date stone of 1857 on the kiln. It was well built in local stone, under a slate roof, but was apparently never used and became a store. In Sherborne, the maltings of the demolished Dorsetshire Brewery in Long Street have been converted to flats, but so completely as to be unrecognisable.

The old malthouse at the end of Fordington High Street, Dorchester.

14

⊰ HEMP AND FLAX INDUSTRIES ⊱

Dorset was said to have produced the best hemp in England, a fact that was certainly never denied in the Bridport area. Hemp and flax were ranked next to quarrying in importance to the trade of the county, and the Bridport district was the focus for making rope, twine and nets since at least the early-thirteenth century. The people of Bridport supplied the navy with its heavy ropes and tackle, and statutes from the time of Henry VIII to James I ensured there was no competition from 5 miles beyond the town. This local monopoly was broken after 1610 when a rope walk was set up for the Navy at Woolwich; others were to follow at Portsmouth and Chatham dockyards. These were much more conveniently placed, more so as the shipping of exceptionally heavy cables from Bridport must have been a formidable task; one only has to inspect HMS *Victory* at Portsmouth for an idea of the sizes involved. Although there was a move away from making cables at Bridport, large ropes were still made for local sailing craft and the ships built at the harbour.

There was a growing market for tackle and nets for the Newfoundland fishery which had been established by Westcountry men in the late-sixteenth century. Dorset ports such as Lyme Regis and Poole were engaged in the fishery, which now became the mainstay of the Bridport industry, and nets, seines, twines and other fishing tackle were shipped out direct to Newfoundland. In 1774 Hutchins remarked that the staple trade of Bridport was in large seines and nets. All manner of other products were made in 1793 when Claridge claimed that nearly 9000 people around Bridport and Beaminster were engaged in some way preparing flax and hemp to manufacture twine, string, carpet thread, pack thread, shoe thread, saddlers' thread, netting, cordage and ropes. Sailcloth of the best quality was woven at home in lengths of 40 yards and a yard wide. Sacking was made for hammocks and grain and flour sacks, and all the processes involved were said to be a 'great support for poor people.' A side industry was the production of linseed oil by beating and pressing the flax seeds in oil mills.

The two families most closely connected with the industry in Bridport were the Gundrys and Hounsells. In 1665 Samuel Gundry had arranged the purchase of hemp for making yarns, twines and nets which he then marketed. Five years later William Hounsell set up in business produc-ing yarns, twines and ropes. As the industry grew the Gundrys came to be involved at Court Mills and Pymore Mills, while the Hounsells were at North Mills.

There were at least 65 different firms of all sizes in the industry in the period 1859–1911, but from then until 1945 their number fell to just 15 after closures and amalgamations. By the late-nineteenth century production had branched out to include nets for cricket, tennis and football, and even billiard table pockets and hammocks. This market was to grow although twines, lines and nets remained the major products. Bridport supplied cordage for the military, as well as camouflage nets, anti-submarine nets and cargo nets during both world wars, but there were slumps afterwards, particularly due to the sale of army surplus goods. Bridport Industries Ltd was formed in 1947 and comprised the numerous firms of William Hounsell & Co. Ltd, Herbert E. Hounsell & Co. Ltd, Ewens & Tucker, Richard Tucker & Sons, William Edwards & Sons, Thomas Budden & Sons, Albert Norman & Son, Rendall & Coombs Ltd, William James & Co. and William Gale & Sons. Meanwhile, Joseph Gundry & Co. had taken over the Pymore Mill Co. Ltd, Thomas Tucker & Co. and Stephen Whetham & Sons. The damaging rivalry between the two groups was eventually solved in 1963 when they amalgamated to form Bridport Gundry Ltd. Modern technology and artificial fibres are now used by Bridport Aviation Products. This most recent name reflects the worldwide importance of high-value cargo and safety netting for aircraft.

After harvesting by hand and threshing the seeds, locally grown hemp and flax were left exposed in the field to be 'dew ripened' to release the strong fibres, but the method of retting was later used when the crop was stacked in tanks or ponds to allow the soft material to rot away. The coarser hemp was best suited to ropes, while the softer and finer texture of flax was better for twine and net making, as well as linens and sailcloth.

Swingling or scutching separated the raw fibres, a process in which machinery was first used at Burton Bradstock in 1803. Balling or bolling further processed the flax and hemp fibres ready for making ropes and twines, by crushing the stems with water-powered tilt hammers. In Bridport, West Mill and Port Mill were balling mills before conversion to corn. By the 1880s the latter was preparing feed for dray horses at the Old

Heckling hemp by hand (from Charles Tomlinson's Cyclopaedia of Useful Arts, *1851)*

Brewery. The Grove iron works had been a balling mill too. Heckling or combing by hand drew out the fibres and removed the short broken fibres ('tow'), but machinery was introduced in the early-nineteenth century. After cleaning, the fibre was spun into yarn on a walk by the operator, who held the fibre wrapped around the waist and fed it out while the spinning wheel was turned by a child.

Spinning rope yarn (from Charles Tomlinson's Cyclopaedia of Useful Arts, *1851)*

Twines, lines and threads were made from two or more yarns twisted together. The yarns were stretched between revolving hooks on a hand-turned jack in the long open walks behind the houses that fronted the streets of Bridport. There were many family rope or twine walks in Bridport, and the last walk closed in 1970. Later rope walks were roofed over as long sheds. Many still existed in 1900 and their numbers are evident on the 25-inch Ordnance Survey maps of that date.

Although some rope and sailcloth were still made in 1900, twine, thread and small cordage were more common; a speciality of Bridport was 'laid twine'. Hemp was now mainly imported from Riga in Russia, sometimes shipped direct to Bridport Harbour but otherwise brought by rail from east-coast ports; likewise, Italian hemp came by rail from London or Liverpool. Flax came from Russia, Belgium and Holland, although some was still acquired from local farms. Trawl lines were still spun by hand with Manila fibre from the Philippines, and cotton was increasingly used for machine-made nets. Drift nets were machine-made, but seines and trawls were still made by hand.

Jumper net-making loom with parts made by Richard R. Samson of Bridport.

Net making was mechanised during the nineteenth century. Net-making machines called 'jumpers' were a Scottish invention but were also manufactured in Bridport, for example by Richard Samson. Such a machine could be installed in a shed at home and the net braider working it was paid by the 'piece' of 50 yards. The foot treadle was heavy and difficult to work so William Hounsell & Co. developed a jumper loom that could be operated by girls. This firm also introduced new methods of line making in the 1870s. Powered net-making machines developed in France at this time could tie up to a thousand knots in a cycle and made sheets of drift nets for the fishing industry, but once off the machine all nets had to be finished off by hand or 'rigged'. The machines were ideal for drift nets of the same width, but nets with square mesh or of variable sizes (like trawls or seines) were still made by hand. Outworkers, mainly women, did much of this net braiding, and the twine was regularly delivered to cottagers in outlying villages and exchanged for finished nets. Different villages specialised in small-mesh or large-mesh nets.

Net-weaving looms at Bridport in about 1900.

BRIDPORT MUSEUM

'The appearance of the town of Bridport bespeaks prosperity by the great improvements made in the buildings within the last twenty years,' wrote John Claridge in 1793. Thereafter, many changes and growth in the industry culminated in the early years of the twentieth century. Despite subsequent closures, amalgamations and redevelopments, parts of Bridport still have more of the feel of an industrial town than anywhere else in Dorset. This legacy of the industry can be seen in buildings such as spinning mills, covered rope and twine walks, weaving or net-making sheds, warehouses and office blocks. Bridport Museum in South Street contains much material relating to the rope and net-making industry.

Machinery for spinning was employed very early in the nineteenth century in the mills at Burton Bradstock and Pymore. Weaving and net making followed and Bridport maintained a leading role in the industry by taking on the challenge of mechanisation. The effect was to bring homeworkers into mills or factories, although it was still possible to retain some independence as an outworker in net braiding or yarn spinning. The earliest machinery was powered by water and some mills retained their wheels well into the twentieth century. Pymore Mill, for example, had a large wheel (17-feet diameter and 16-feet wide) down to the time of closure in the 1950s. The 'Return of Mills & Factories' of 1838 recorded eight waterwheels powering flax mills around Bridport and Burton Bradstock, in addition to three steam engines.

Priory Mill *(SY 464927)* was the first purpose-built steam-powered factory in Bridport, built in 1838 by Stephen Whetham & Sons for making lines, twines and canvas. Although now put to other uses, and its machinery scrapped, this prominent stone building is a fitting reminder of the town's industrial past. A tall round-headed window indicates the site of the 82hp beam engine, which drove machinery for balling, heckling, carding, drawing, roving and spinning flax and tow, and machinery for cabling, twisting and polishing. There were also net-braiding machines and 17 heavy canvas looms. Whethams had an impressive stone warehouse of 1862 at the corner

Priory Mill was the first purpose-built steam-powered mill in Bridport. It was built in 1838 by Stephen Whetham & Sons for making lines, twines and canvas. The tall arched window at the far end was for the engine room.

Stephen Whetham & Sons' large warehouse off Gundry Lane was built in the same local stone as for Priory Mill.

the merger with the Gundrys. The St Michael's Works *(SY 464928)* is the most distinctive building, in red brick with a tower. This was built in the early-twentieth century for William Edwards, an important manufacturer of nets whose firm is still supplying the sports trade from a site at North Mills. To the north is a complex of former covered spinning walks owned at various

of Rope Walks and Gundry Lane *(SY 465928)*, which is now conserved.

The nearby St Michael's Trading Estate was the main site of Bridport Industries before

times by William Gale, Ewens & Turner and Robert Hounsell & Sons. Of special interest is a tar house, necessary for the proofing of netting and cordage before the advent of artificial fibres.

St Michael's Works was built in about 1900 for the net-making firm of William Edwards.

The tar house is an interesting survival among the old works in the St Michael's Trading Estate. Note the roof ventilators.

The Court Works (SY 464931) was the headquarters of the Gundrys, now Bridport Aviation Products. There was a damaging fire in 1949, but some historic buildings remain such as the stone office block of 1844 fronting the north side of West Street, and a brick warehouse dated 1811. William Hounsell & Co.

made lines, twines and nets at North Mills (SY 465935), where their factory was powered by two steam engines and a waterwheel. The site has been broken up for different industrial uses, but remaining structures include hemp stores, a long covered twine walk and net-weaving sheds.

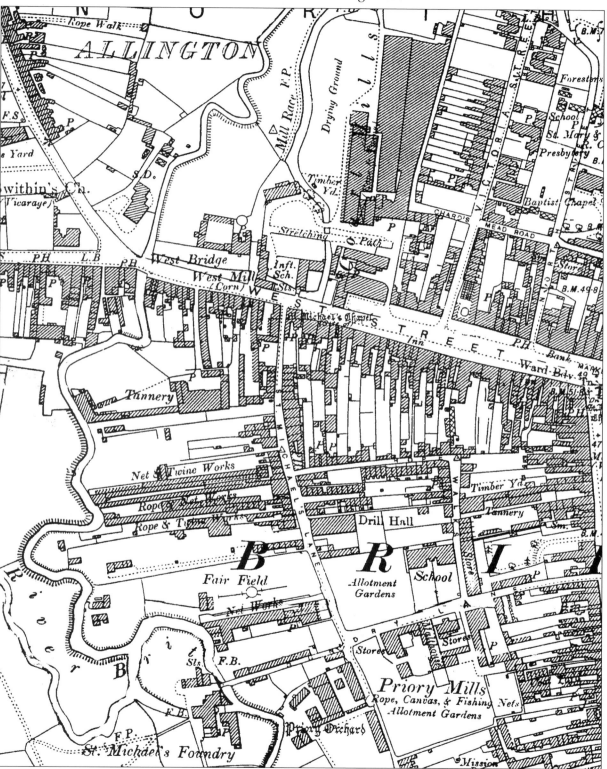

The St Michael's area of Bridport in 1900, from the Ordnance Survey 25-inch map. Long covered rope walks are clearly seen in the building plans and, although much altered, this distinctive pattern is still recognisable today.

The office building of Court Mill on West Street was the headquarters of the Gundry family, later Bridport Gundry Ltd and, more recently, Bridport Aviation Products.

The covered rope or twine walk at North Mills, Bridport. Such buildings are not always easy to convert but this one has survived.

The Pymore Mills and warehouses near Bridport.

A self-contained industrial village was just north of Bridport at Pymore. There is enough left of the mills and village at Pymore *(SY 470946)* to see its industrial origins engaged in flax, hemp, net and rope manufacturing. The Pymore Mill Co. chose the site beside the River Brit for water power, and converted a linseed oil and grist mill to flax spinning in the early-1800s. The powerful waterwheel was scrapped after the mill burnt down in 1959. There was a steam-powered flax mill here in the 1830s, and this compact site included stables, dyeing room, rope walk, manager's house and a terrace of workers' cottages. Mrs Gundry built a small school in 1870 in memory of her son who drowned at West Bay. At the start of the twenty-first century, much of the village was under redevelopment for housing. Some buildings were retained but the rope walk was demolished.

Burton Bradstock was a less developed industrial village, where Richard Roberts was involved in flax spinning and manufacturing in the early-nineteenth century and transformed the village's flax industry from a craft to factory basis. In 1794 he opened a spinning mill on the River Bride and built a nearby terrace of cottages for weavers in 1800. Three years later he built Grove Mill *(SY 490897)* for flax swingling in an early attempt to mechanise the preparation of flax. In 1814

Roberts built a third mill for spinning and claimed to employ 200 looms for weaving, which would be in cottages in the village and surrounding district. He died in 1818 and his son Francis sold the mills in 1840. Grove Mill became a corn mill, and its waterwheel was replaced in 1946 by a 15hp Armfield turbine when it was worked by the Rendall family. Since closed and converted to housing, this renamed 'Burton Mill' has a stone set in a wall reading: 'This flax-swingling mill, the first introduced into the West of England, was erected by Richard Roberts, 1803.' Downstream, the flax-spinning mill at the end of Mill Street was later occupied by Messrs Rendall & Coombs from 1898 until 1931. It is now derelict but Roberts' row of cottages is occupied close by the churchyard wall, and an inscription 'RR 1800' provides the date.

Richard Roberts used flax mostly from local sources but also imported it via London from the Russian Baltic. His manufactured sailcloth was sold at ports in the South West as well as London and Portsmouth. He did not confine his activities just to sailcloth and offered a fascinating range including duck, sheetings, table linen, napkins, wrapping and packing cloths, bread bags, hammocks, canvas, shop bagging, wool bags, wick yarn, cheesecloth, coffee bags, shoe thread and hand towels. He also sold flax seed, especially to Belfast via London.

Sailcloth was an important product at Beaminster and mills were established in the area for preparing and spinning the flax. In 1793 Samuel Cox was said to employ 'upwards of 600 people' in manufacturing sailcloth at Beaminster. In 1838 there were 120 looms employed in the sailcloth trade in the district. Thomas Frampton & Son took over the Cox's Fleet Street factory and also acquired a flax mill at Whatley in 1836. Six years later they were still making sailcloth, but this side of the industry was 'almost extinct.' By the 1860s Whatley Mill was a corn mill, but Cox's works may have existed until the 1870s. Manufacturing returned to Whatley Mill for a few years when flax was grown in the area during the First World War. Other flax mills in the district included Slape Mill on the River Brit, with Horsehill Mill and Clenham Mill on a tributary between Stoke Abbott and Netherbury. Mills at Mosterton and Greenham (1825) also produced flax, and sailcloth was manufactured at Broadwindsor until at least 1895. To the southeast, one of the twin mills at Mangerton (SY 490957) was a flax mill, later becoming a balling mill.

West Dorset did not have the entire monopoly of the hemp and flax industry. In Purbeck, William Morton Pitt attempted to give employment to the poor at Kingston by establishing a rope and sailcloth factory in the late-eighteenth century, but it soon failed. Ropes and sailcloth were also made at Poole. Ticking and dowlas (a coarse linen for smocks) were woven at Bourton, Gillingham, Silton, Cerne Abbas and Melbury Osmond, this last being the source of a stay-makers' tape known as 'Melbury iron tape'. Many years later, the former brewery at Fontmell Magna was used as a flax mill briefly in the mid-twentieth century. The main district, however, was around Bourton in the north, where two flax mills were worked by members of the Maggs family.

The industry at Bourton in the early-nineteenth century used locally grown flax and yarn imported from Holland. Bullpits House, which is said to have been a flax mill in the eighteenth century, stands above the large Factory Pond and remains of the Maggs' flax mill and foundry (ST 775312) where a 60-foot diameter waterwheel was erected in 1837. Five years later, Daniel Maggs was listed as a tick, dowlas, sailcloth and shoe thread manufacturer, and Oliver Maggs was listed until the early-1880s as a flax spinner and sack manufacturer. A second flax mill (ST 777309) was occupied by William Jesse, a tick and dowlas manufacturer, before 1851 when Uriah Maggs leased the factory with engine room and wheel. The latter was a sacking manufacturer, flax, tow, hemp and jute spinner, and linen-yarn merchant in 1875, but work had ceased by 1885. This High Street factory's waterwheel had a poor water supply from an aqueduct and narrow millpond above. It was much altered over the years and a steam engine was installed, perhaps in the 1850s. It is now a private house.

There was a rope walk just below the Bourton flax mill and foundry site in 1885, where Moore & Farthing were recorded as rope and twine makers; Walter Farthing continued here until at least 1903.

Advertisement for Walter Tucker, net-maker of Bridport, 1889.

15

❧ WOOLLEN AND SILK TEXTILES ❧

The West of England woollen textile industry reached down into neighbouring Wiltshire and parts of Somerset but was never so important in Dorset. Nevertheless, the chalk downs were home to thousands of sheep – Daniel Defoe was told of 600,000 sheep within a 6-mile radius of Dorchester if he can be believed – and their fleeces provided the raw material for a broadcloth made mostly for local consumption.

In 1793 Claridge wrote that about 1200 people were employed in Sturminster and the surrounding villages making swanskin, a coarse white flannel used for soldiers' clothing. Spinners and weavers worked from home to produce up to 5000 pieces of 35 yards every year. Upwards of 1000 women and children were engaged in knitting worsted stockings at Wimborne. Twenty years later, Stevenson noted that broadcloth and flannel were confined to Sturminster and Lyme Regis. The former town had about 300 weavers and up to 800 persons were employed occasionally but the trade was in decline. Woollen cloth was also made at Beaminster, and stockings were knitted 'in great abundance' for sale at Wimborne and Wareham. These were all cottage industries and had largely died out before the age of factories.

From the fourteenth century water-powered fulling or tucking mills pounded woven cloth to thicken the fabric and remove excess grease, and examples are known at Bridport, Cerne Abbas, Lyme Regis and Wareham. Louds Mill (*ST 709903*), just below Dorchester, was a late-sixteenth-century fulling mill. William Stanton was described as a 'woollen cloth manufacturer' here in 1830, but substantial textile mills were only built for the flax industries (as described above) and for silk.

The Dorset silk industry lasted for a period of 200 years and was mostly confined to the north around Sherborne and Gillingham where mills were established for throwing or spinning the imported raw silk. Sherborne was the scene of the most successful silk textile industry, which began in 1753 when John Sharrer, a silk throwster from Whitechapel, acquired a grist mill on the River Yeo at Westbury, with a house and land. Within a few years he spent £2500 rebuilding Westbury Mill and fitting it out with water-powered machinery for silk throwing. Bales of raw silk were brought down from London, having been imported from Italy, China, Bengal and Turkey. The throwsters used an 'engine' to wind

Silk doubling or throwing (from Charles Tomlinson's Cyclopaedia of Useful Arts, *1851)*

skeins of silk onto bobbins before being twisted, or thrown. The raw silk was also cleaned at this stage, removing as much as 18 per cent waste. By 1765 Sharrer was claimed to be employing 400 workers in Dorset, and some 1100 others in his interests in London, Gloucestershire and Cheshire; these were almost entirely women and children. He had entered a partnership with his nephews George Ward and William Willmott but, two years after he had died in 1767, Willmott took over the Sherborne mill and other small silk works at Cerne Abbas and Stalbridge. His cousin moved to a silk mill at Bruton in Somerset.

William Willmott ran an efficient business that remained in the family for over a century. Problems with water shortages were partly overcome by installing a larger wheel and a horse mill to drive some of the machinery when needed. William died in 1787 and was succeeded by his son Thomas who led the business until his own death in 1851. Trade was variable in the early-nineteenth century and in 1832 Thomas Willmott reported to a Parliamentary inquiry into the silk trade that six years earlier there had been 8000 spindles and 600 employed, but now there were only 3000 spindles and 150 employees, of whom two-thirds were homeworkers. By then they were using mainly Italian silk.

Trade must have picked up by the 1840s when a new two-storey silk mill (*ST 635159*) was built on a new site at the junction of Westbury and Ottery Lane (formerly Factory Lane). It was powered by a shaft under the road from Westbury Mill. The editors of the 1873 edition of Hutchins' Dorset history wrote that 'West Mill is a very spacious building, in two floors, well lighted and ventilated

The two and three-storey silk mill range at Westbury, Sherborne, was built in about 1840 by Thomas Willmott. It has been converted into small industrial units of the Old Yarn Mills Business Centre.

The Westbury silk mill range, seen from the north.

and fitted with machinery worked by steam power.' This is now the Old Yarn Mills Business Centre, having been adapted to small industrial use.

John and Robert Willmott took over on their father's death in 1851, but the industry was in trouble. By 1875 Albert Willmott had inherited a failing industry and the mill nearly closed. Ten years later, when there was much distress and unemployment in the town, the Rev. Joseph Ogle of the Congregational Church formed J. & R. Willmott Ltd and after two years of hard work the first silk was produced. Ogle's brother-in-law Samuel le Mare from Macclesfield (a silk town) ran the mill. Silk was also being woven here and in 1899 material made for Queen Victoria's dresses must have been a bonus to this local industry.

The twentieth century brought changes and the mill was sold in 1907 to A. & R. Wright & Co. of Bingley, who continued weaving until 1936. The new purchaser, H. Spitz of Switzerland, failed financially despite fitting out the mill with the latest Swiss looms. It was fortunate for Sherborne that the mill was purchased in 1937 by Frederick Marsden, who owned a rayon mill in Coventry, and within a year production was under way again. War work soon followed, when Marsden turned to weaving parachute silk and introduced rayon weaving which required new methods. More importantly, the innovative Marsden developed fine silk for electrical insulation in military hardware, where previously this had come from Japan. He also developed weaveable glass yarn for electrical insulation in 1942, and the firm became known as Marglass Ltd after the war.

There was expansion in the 1950s when the River Yeo was diverted away to make more room on the site. The first Westbury Mill, sold off in 1916, was bought back to serve as a workshop (this was later burnt out). Silk weaving ceased by 1956, but Marglass Ltd thrived. After several takeovers the company was bought by Clark-Schwebel Ltd, the world's largest woven fibreglass fabric makers, and today CS Interglas Ltd at Sherborne operate the largest mill of its type in Britain.

There were smaller silk mills elsewhere in Sherborne. Abbey Mill was converted to silk briefly in 1775 to 1793, and was apparently bought out by Thomas Willmott, although John Gouger was recorded here in 1830. The building had been part of the abbey guesthouse, and was incorporated into Sherborne School in the later-nineteenth century. The Willmotts' silk throwing business expanded with the acquisition of East or Castle Mill in 1809 and Oke's or Middle Mill in 1814. East Mill was sold to the Salisbury & Yeovil Railway Co., who demolished it to make way for their new line which opened in 1860.

A smaller, but important silk mill was established in 1769 in the centre of Gillingham (ST 808266). The Gillingham Silk Co. was a partnership of Stephen Hannam, a Quaker and miller, Joseph Whitehead, a clothier of Bruton, and William Tinney and John Daniel, gentlemen of Gillingham and Yeovil. The new mill was built next to Hannam's Town Mill on Shreen Water, a tributary of the Stour. It was furnished with water-powered machinery for silk throwing and it was agreed that in times of water shortage the silk mill would have precedence over the corn mill. The partnership was dissolved in 1776 and Hannam continued until his death in 1780. Thereafter, the mill was run by his widow Catherine for four years, their son Josiah Hannam to 1828, and then his son Samuel until 1840 when his brother went into partnership with a nephew Thomas Thompson. After they died in the early-1870s, Samuel Hannam Stephens carried on until the Gillingham silk mill closed in 1895.

Early in the nineteenth century about 160 were employed, many working at home in surrounding villages winding the raw skeins onto bobbins ready for throwing and cleaning in the mill. A large number of girls were apprenticed from London workhouses 'to learn the art and mystery of a silk throwster'. They were favoured because their slender fingers could handle the very fine threads, and they provided cheap labour. Examples of indentures of the early-1780s record girls from St Leonards, Shoreditch, Middlesex, aged nine to fifteen being signed on until the age of twenty-one or marriage. The apprentice girls lived in the upper floor of a building just to the west and at right angles to the mill. On the ground floor were washing and drying rooms.

The twentieth century was one of decline and increasing dereliction. After a number of subsequent uses, which included T.H. Brickell's printing works in the dormitory wing, the old Town Mill became empty and fire-torn before the whole site was demolished in 1988 for redevelopment. Shreen Water had powered two other silk mills, but in Wiltshire. These were Hincke's Mill and Lord's Mill, higher up the stream towards Mere, worked by Charles Jupe & Son, who had more silk mills at Warminster.

T.H. Brickell established a printing works in part of the Gillingham silk mill after it closed in 1895. He is seen in 1910 with his staff at the waterwheel which was shared by the adjacent corn mill.

16

❧ FOUNDERS AND ENGINEERS ❧

Engineering activities in the period ranged from the village blacksmith to iron founders, machine makers and electrical engineers. The twentieth century saw a new body of engineers in the motor trade, and a number of garages had their origins with a smithy. The small garage for motor repairs and petrol sales had become a familiar part of the village scene in the 1950s but is now rapidly disappearing.

The iron foundries and their products, however, are most closely associated with the Age of Steam. Most towns had an agricultural engineer or small foundry in the nineteenth century, making a wide range of machinery and cast-iron items. Some were short-lived, but others survived to grow into successful engineering works manufacturing specialist products with markets far from Dorset.

Methods of working were similar whatever the size of the foundry. Iron and fuel always had to be bought in, as was the brass used by some founders. Wooden patterns made up in the pattern maker's shop were kept for many years for future use. In the moulding shop, the patterns were set in special sand in box moulds that were taken to the casting shop where the iron was melted in a cupola furnace with a blast powered by water or steam. A crucible furnace was used in a brass foundry. The molten metal was carefully poured into the mould and once it was cool the rough casting was broken out of the mould and taken to be 'fettled' in the finishing shop. Larger castings were made in a sand pit in the floor. Where different parts of a machine or steam engine were involved they were taken to the erecting or machine shop where they were put together. Wrought iron was also involved in some work. Small jobbing foundries made items to order for other manufacturers. Just about every shape and size was possible for a skilled founder and the list is immense. Many examples were cast with their maker's name and are proof today that the founders' products were by no means confined to their own area. Typical common products were items of street furniture, such as drain covers, manhole covers, lampposts, drinking troughs, fountains, mile posts and road signs.

Early agricultural engineers included Maggs at Bourton and Coombes at Beaminster, both of whom had made threshing machines in the early-1800s. All kinds of agricultural implements were later supplied, including ploughs, harrows, rakes,

rollers, mowers and chaff-cutters. Smaller items were cheese presses (an example by Pond & Son of Blandford is displayed in the Dorset County Museum at Dorchester). The extensive water meadow systems of the chalk valleys required ironwork for hatches, and examples were made by John Galpin of Dorchester.

Iron waterwheels were made by several founders or millwrights in the nineteenth century. For example, Winter & Hossey of Dorchester supplied the large wheel at Maiden Newton Mill, a wheel at French Mill, Shaftesbury, and others on farms at Forston, Hewish and Trigon. Much later, Henry George Martin supplied two waterwheels to Winterbourne Steepleton Mill. Charles Coombs was a millwright in North Street, Beaminster, from at least 1823, and his firm's waterwheels survive at Chetnole Mill (1848), Litton Cheney Mill (1866) and West Mill, Sherborne (1877). Maggs and Hindley of Bourton were also known for their wheels.

Daniel Maggs established a foundry and agricultural engineering works *(ST 775310)* next to his Bourton corn and flax mills in the early-1800s. He is known to have made at least two threshing machines, but almost certainly made others. A damaged iron waterwheel cast 'D. Maggs. 1819' from Nether Cerne Manor Farm is now preserved at the Castleton Water Museum in Sherborne, and this significant wheel may be the oldest dated all-iron survivor in the West Country.

By 1842, Oliver and George Maggs were listed as 'brass and ironfounders and machine makers' but Oliver was in complete control from 1848–59, described as an 'ironfounder, engineer and agricultural implement maker', as well as owning the grist and flax mills. Edmund Samuel Hindley became a partner in about 1860, the firm trading as Maggs & Hindley (one of their wheels at Old Barn, Stalbridge, is dated 1862). Hindley had taken over by 1867 when 'millwright' was added to his activities, and in 1870 he was advertising portable and fixed steam engines, hydraulic cider presses, portable cider presses and mills, cider screws, apple mills, and several second-hand engines for sale. By the end of the century his sons had been taken into partnership.

There are surviving examples of E.S. Hindley's waterwheels made for local corn mills at Melbury Abbas (1875), Cann (1880s), Stour Provost (1889), and West Mill, Stalbridge

(1893). A 16-feet diameter high-breastshot waterwheel with a pump installed at Maiden Bradley in 1902 are now displayed at the Kew Bridge Steam Museum, London. Nearer home, in fact just upstream from the foundry, is an overshot pumping waterwheel of 1921 at Stourhead in Wiltshire; a smaller wheel here does not have the maker's name. This shows that E.S. Hindley & Sons were still making wheels despite manufacturing more sophisticated engineering products, and their skills were also called upon at Sherborne for maintaining the Castleton waterworks wheel and pump.

By the 1870s the Bourton foundry was making boilers and vertical and horizontal steam engines. A necessary part of the business in the early-twentieth century was a showroom at 11 Queen Victoria Street in London, when E.S. Hindley & Sons were manufacturing steam lorries, gas and oil engines, pumps, dynamos, hoists and saw benches. It is hard to envisage today that a successful engineering works in this quiet corner of rural Dorset employed up to 200 workers and exported its products all over the world. The firm was bought out in 1927 by Alfred Dodman of King's Lynn, who continued to build the Hindley oil engine there for another thirty years, which is a tribute to its good design and reliability.

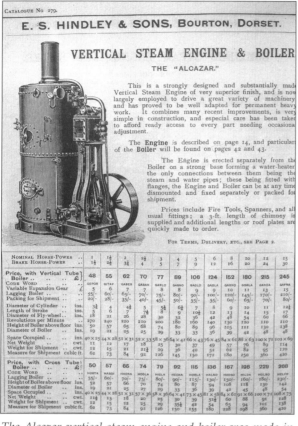

The Alcazar vertical steam engine and boiler was made in different sizes by E.S. Hindley of Bourton. From a trade catalogue.

A steam lorry waits in the yard at Bourton foundry where it was manufactured for the Dorchester Roller Flour Mills, early-twentieth century.

The busy Bourton iron foundry is seen occupying a narrow valley below the fields in about 1900.

GILLINGHAM MUSEUM

There are at least 110 workers in this view of Hindley's foundry yard in the small village of Bourton in the early-twentieth century. Note the water-wheel on the left.

The closure of the foundry caused much unemployment in Bourton which was only relieved in 1933 when the site became a milk products factory. There are still traces of the foundry and adjacent flax mill buildings, although much altered, as well as the large Factory Pond. A giant 60-feet diameter waterwheel advertised the skill of Maggs from 1837 until 1918 and it has left enough marks on a wall beside the wheelpit to confirm its large diameter. There were two much smaller waterwheels at Bourton and two Armfield turbines were installed in 1920–21, not long before the foundry's closure. Naturally, there was steam power too.

At the Bourton foundry site.

Two of E.S. Hindley & Sons' small steam engines are preserved in Dorset. One at the Weymouth Brewery (Brewer's Quay) was made in about 1890, while a very late product is a 'No.5 Alcazar' steam pump made in 1925 for pumping tar and waste liquids at Sherborne gasworks and now in Sherborne Museum. Other 'Alcazar' donkey engines are displayed at the Black Country Museum in Dudley and the Hereford Waterworks Museum. The latter was installed in 1911 to work a brine pump at Tenbury Wells spa. Other Bourton products known to survive vary from a cast-iron pipe by Oliver Maggs at the Sutton Poyntz Water Supply Museum, to a Maggs & Hindley water trough at Enmore Green, Shaftesbury, a 30-foot waterwheel at Tavistock in Devon, and various agricultural implements.

Another success story in a small rural village in north Dorset was the establishment of a works for manufacturing brewing equipment at Fontmell Magna. John Walter Flower was a trained brewer who took over the Fontmell Magna Brewery with his brother on the death of their father in 1879. He devised a number of useful inventions for that industry and had the confidence to set up the Springhead Works in 1885, with a partner R.J.

Cousins, at the old Higher Mill where an overshot wheel provided the power. Machines were displayed at exhibitions, where the 'Eclipse automatic filling and corking machine' and the 'Lightning dry hopper' won gold medals. The business grew on these successes and the firm employed 33 men when it outgrew the premises and transferred the Eclipse Works to a larger and better location at Wimborne in 1906. Bottling and labelling machines were designed and manufactured until 1966, although during both world wars the factory was turned over to manufacturing munitions. The Springhead buildings are now an environmental centre but the Wimborne site is no more.

There were two main foundries at Poole. The Poole Foundry was set up by William Pearce in an old rope works in the early-1840s to manufacture agricultural machinery. Some products were shown at the Great Exhibition of 1851, before the foundry was bought in 1863 by Stephen Lewin with William Wilkinson, a Boston engineer. Five years later James Welman was appointed manager and the foundry was thriving, making drainpipes, window frames, grating and steam-powered agricultural machinery during a short-lived farming boom. This machinery included portable engines, threshing machines, saw tables and Lewin's 'patent folding stacker and elevator' which won a 'grand and special prize for merit' at the Vienna Exhibition in 1873. William Tarrant from Devizes was manager in 1873 and began making narrow-gauge steam locomotives and larger contractors' and colliery locomotives. Customers included the Guinness Brewery in Dublin and Seaham Harbour in County Durham. More locally, the 'Tiny' was built for the Goathorn clay railway. One section of the works specialised in steam yachts and launches.

Lewin developed an export trade (his catalogue was printed in ten languages), and when the foundry was seriously damaged by fire 1876, a boat for Brazil and six threshing machines for Russia were destroyed. Fifty steam engines were also lost and, more seriously, so were the foundry's tools and patterns. Lewin was not fully insured and the business never recovered. Welman returned but both men were bankrupted; the foundry was sold in 1884 and houses were built on the site *(SZ 013908)*. A second Poole Foundry off Thames Street *(SZ 008904)* worked as a jobbing foundry from about 1930 until 1985.

The Dorset Foundry was established by Munden & Stricklen in West Quay Road *(SZ 006905)* in the 1850s, and was bought by Charles Stone in 1870. William Tarrant moved here after the fire at Lewin's foundry and bought it with partners in

Workers in the Lott & Walne foundry at Dorchester in about 1900.

1879, forming the Dorset Iron Foundry Co. Ltd. They gained from the closure of Lewin's foundry and the Dorset Foundry continued until the late-1950s. The Waterloo Foundry, previously in Hatch Pond Road, was at West Quay Road from about 1888 until closure in 1901. Described as iron and brass founders and mechanical engineers manufacturing agricultural and dairy appliances, steam engines and boilers, they were also contractors for piers at Southbourne (1888), Boscombe (1889) and Sandbanks (1898).

John Galpin had an iron foundry in Fordington, Dorchester, from about 1840 until 1875 when it was taken over by Messrs Lott & Walne. Little is known of Galpin's business but his products varied from water meadow hatches at Toller Fratrum and Puddletown, to a crane's hand-winch at Durdle Pier on Portland, all of which bear his name on the casting. Lott & Walne expanded the business and their name appears on all sorts of agricultural equipment: ring drives for waterwheels, sluices, drain covers and other street furniture, including a sturdy lamppost in front of the Dorchester Brewery in Weymouth Avenue. Their spring-mounted water carts, drawn by horses, were popular with local authorities throughout England. Liquid manure and tumbler carts were also advertised in 1911, with portable houses, shepherd's

appliances and 'perfect automatic lamb creeps'. A collection of wooden patterns dating from 1875 to 1932 kept by the Dorset County Museum provides further evidence of their range of products. Turning more to agricultural engineering in the twentieth century, Lott & Walne Ltd stopped iron casting and finally left the foundry in 1988. Today, the three-storey brick building (*SY 696907*) has been saved from demolition by its conversion into flats. The exterior is intact, with 'The Foundry, Lott & Walne Limited' still painted on the wall fronting Fordington High Street, where a simple crane once lifted materials into the upper floors. Sadly, the works bell on a roof gable was removed shortly after the foundry was closed.

A typical advertisement for Lott & Walne in 1903.

The Lott & Walne foundry at Fordington, Dorchester, derelict in 1985.

The old Lott & Walne foundry has been converted into flats but retains the crane and painted name along Fordington High Street, Dorchester.

Francis Eddison established a steam plough works in Wareham Road at Fordington in 1868 and two years later two ploughing sets with Fowler engines were described at work on farms at Coker's Frome and Stratton. In February 1885 Eddison had 12 steam ploughs for hire when the *Dorset County Chronicle* described the works:

> *The long array of engines, and the formidable assemblage of steam ploughs, together with the vast quantity of accessory apparatus, such as sleeping vans, water carts, trucks, etc, to be seen in the yard, at once show the dimensions to which the business has arrived … In truth, the works now constitute one of the largest manufactories in the town.*

Eddison was employing 60–70 men and the long range of workshops housed powerful steam lathes and drilling machines. Steam ploughing was suffering from the agricultural depression at this time, but Eddison was also a contractor for steam threshing and haulage. More importantly, in 1882

he bought the first steam roadroller to be operated on hire in England, driving it home personally from Aveling & Porter's factory at Rochester. The Eddison Steam Rolling Co. Ltd was formed in 1901, the ploughing and traction engines being sold off in the 1920s, after which the firm concentrated on hiring rollers and their living vans. Eddison Plant Ltd, formed in 1946, became a leading contractor of rollers, compressors and other construction equipment, with 20 depots throughout Britain.

Bridport is also known for its foundries. The Grove Iron Works at West Allington (*SY 454931*) was established by Robert Sprake in 1809, taking the premises of a former bolling mill. He died in 1833, and his son Henry worked on until his own death in 1838. A very large Sprake waterwheel survives at Toller Fratrum Farm, and 'H. Sprake 1833' is cast on an outsized drainpipe between the two thatched gables of the Old Brewery in West Bay Road. Gerard Samson next took the works, making agricultural and industrial machinery, including a net-making machine now in Bridport Museum. His sons joined him in the 1870s and by the time of his death in 1880, they were making steam engines, rollers, harrows and threshing machines. A waterwheel for Town Mill, Lyme Regis, was made in 1888 but no longer survives. After 1889, Richard Samson expanded the business to include more net-making machines and kitchen ranges. The river sluices for the Old Brewery waterwheel are by Samson, as are two pillars of the 1899 gasworks' showroom in South Street. Paragon Engineering occupied the works from about 1922 making kitchen ranges, drain covers and other products, and after the Second World War the Grove Works became a jobbing foundry. The foundry is a rare survival today, modern furnaces are employed to make iron, bronze and aluminium castings for industrial and architectural purposes.

Thomas Helyear's name and date 1879 are cast on the waterwheel at the Old Brewery. He had gained experience as an engineer elsewhere, returning to Bridport in 1860 as an engineer and machinist. From 1871 his foundry at 54 West Street was manufacturing net-making machines (one is in the Science Museum) and the above-mentioned wheel. After he died in 1905, George Bonfield bought out the stock and set up an iron and brass foundry at 66 West Street; he was described as a motor engineer in 1911. Herbert Harris established the St Michael's Foundry in a former canvas factory in 1889, and installed a water turbine for power. Agricultural and industrial products were made, including a rope-making jack preserved in Bridport Museum. Harris also hired out traction engines and threshing machines. After he died in 1924 the site continued as an engineering works for a while. Foundry Lane is now the only reminder of the site.

Cosens & Co. Ltd, the paddle-steamer owners, had an engineering and ship repair works on the Backwater and slipways on the south side of the harbour at Weymouth. In the same town, Daniel Collett was a 'manufacturer of every description of cast and wrought iron, machinery, cranes, crabs, pumps, etc, for manufacturing, quarrying, shipping and other purposes' in the period

1855–85. A rare fragment of a quarry crane on Portland bears his name. The Easton Foundry on Portland supplied the stone industry with parts for cranes and wagons, as well as quarrying tools. No cranes survive, alas, but the name of the foundry can still be seen on drain covers and stench pipes around the island.

Founders from just outside the county were close enough to compete with Dorset foundries. Agricultural machinery was supplied by Dening & Co. of Chard, Somerset, and turbines and milling equipment came from Joseph Armfield of Ringwood, Hampshire. Edward Cockey & Sons of Frome in Somerset manufactured the cast-iron pillars for the main gallery of the Dorset County Museum in 1883, but other products include mileposts on the turnpike road through Shaftesbury (now the A30), and a weighbridge at Castle Farm, Buckland Newton.

Advertisement for Daniel Collett, iron founder of Weymouth in 1865.

THE FOUNDRY, WEYMOUTH.

DANIEL COLLETT,

ENGINEER, IRON AND BRASS FOUNDER;

MANUFACTURER OF

EVERY DESCRIPTION OF CAST & WROUGHT IRON,

MACHINERY, CRANES, CRABS, PUMPS, &c., &c.,

FOR

Manufacturing, Quarrying, Shipping and other Purposes.

GENERAL SMITH'S WORK EXECUTED ON THE

Shortest Notice and Most Reasonable Terms.

The main outside supplier of milling equipment, turbines and water sluices in Dorset was Joseph Armfield of Ringwood, Hampshire. However, this cast-iron hurst frame at Cann Mills was made by W. Tasker & Sons of Andover.

17

FOOD PROCESSING AND PAPER MAKING

Food processing and paper making are just two examples of Dorset's many lesser-known miscellaneous industries. Food processing is, naturally, one of the most vital of all industries, yet it has received remarkably little attention from historians or industrial archaeologists. The next step on from corn milling was bread baking. This was usually done in the home but some corn mills had bakeries attached. For example, Samuel Moores first made the famous 'Dorset knob' biscuits in a bakehouse at Stoke Mill near Broadoak in the Marshwood Vale. Moores worked the mill from the late-1850s to produce flour for his bakehouse, before moving to the present biscuit bakery at Morcombelake in 1879. The Rendalls' mill at Burton Bradstock had a bakery in the 1930s and there was also a bakery at Hembury Mill, Askerswell, until 1940. Battrick's bakery in the cottage at Boar Mill, Corfe Castle, continued until about 1960. Some flour produced at Throop Mill was used for making ships' biscuits locally in the nineteenth century, and Parsons & Sons used the mill to supply their bakery business when they bought it 1926.

The old bakehouse at Stoke Mill in the Marshwood Vale was occupied by Samuel Moores from about 1860 before he moved to the present famous bakery at Morecombelake in 1879.

Cheese making was traditionally a farm-based industry, but one effect of the railways was to open up new markets for cheese, butter and liquid milk, and in turn the farm dairies were replaced by the building of milk depots, dairies or creameries in the later-nineteenth century. The delivery of milk churns became a familiar scene on rural station platforms until the introduction of milk tank wagons at dairy companies' sidings and, finally, road tankers.

The Blackmoor Vale provides a good example of a once thriving milk, cheese and butter industry. This was Hardy's 'Vale of the Little Dairies' and in 1848 the dairies around Gillingham were said to be a principal source of wealth to the town. The opening of the railway to London in 1859 brought new opportunities for the milk and dairy trade here, which was repeated in other centres which had access to rail. Eden Joseph Shute built a butter factory in New Road in 1892, with power from a Crossley gas engine. His successful Golden Melon brand of butter was sold locally as well as in London shops. A milk factory was built in about 1880 by Messrs Shute and Sims in Wyke Street. The building, noted for its thick stone and brick walls, later became a glove factory *(ST 806265)*.

Workers at the Salisbury, Semley & Gillingham Dairies milk factory in Station Road, Gillingham, in 1906. Note the milk churns, typical of the period.

GILLINGHAM MUSEUM

In 1885 the Salisbury, Semley & Gillingham Dairies Ltd had a large depot at Gillingham for making cheese and supplying milk to London. This firm had opened the first ever railway milk depot in 1871 opposite Semley Station (just inside Wiltshire), especially to serve the London market. United Dairies took over the milk and cheese factory in Station Road at Gillingham in 1920. It had a transport department, cheese cellars and a tinsmith shop for making milk churns. The long range had a manager's house at one end and a central archway. Cheese making ceased before the Second World War, after which parts became the Gillingham & District Modern Laundry, an egg-packing station and furniture store. The north section, including the manager's house, has been demolished but the words 'United Dairies Ltd Head Office Trowbridge, Wilts' can be discerned over the entrance arch *(ST 809262)*.

United Dairies had its origins in Wiltshire in the later-nineteenth century and acquired depots and dairies in Dorset in the 1920s, including Maiden Newton, Wimborne and Sturminster Marshall. This last, at Bailey Gate, became an important milk distribution centre with sidings from the Somerset & Dorset Railway. There were other dairies along this line at Shillingstone, Stalbridge and Sturminster Newton.

The successful Sturminster Newton Creamery (ST 789143) was established close to the station in 1913 by Sturminster Newton & District Farmers Ltd, a farmers' co-operative, but was taken over by Dairy Crest in 1937. Milk was delivered by lorry in churns from surrounding farms and award-winning cheese was manufactured. A coal-fired boiler provided steam for pasteurisation and hot water for cleaning and heating. Bulk tankers brought in the milk by the time the creamery was closed in 2000.

The unusual ventilated roof-line of the Oake-Woods bacon factory near the railway station at Gillingham, is seen in 1986. This once important factory has since been demolished.

Gillingham was also known for the Oake-Woods bacon factory (ST 809261). This was established in 1847, and it was good fortune that the railway was built alongside twelve years later. Oake Woods & Co. grew to be a major employer in the town, with a workforce of 150. The factory had its own well and the extensive cellars were said to be the best in the country for curing. Oake invented the 'Auto-Cure' method for curing bacon in pressure cylinders and the Danes paid a high royalty for its use. Such was the quality of its products that the firm received a royal appointment to King Edward VII. The business was owned by C. & T. Harris of Calne by the 1950s. The factory closed in about 1980 and most of the site was later demolished.

Paper making is one of Dorset's lost industries, the last mill at Witchampton having closed in the 1980s. The chalk streams provided the necessary clear water and also provided the power for the waterwheels working the pulping and beating machinery. Raw materials included locally grown flax in west Dorset, where there was a paper mill at Beaminster from the mid-eighteenth century until about 1814. Old sailcloth, rope and rags were also used and could be obtained from the port at Bridport. Poole also provided these materials, and there were small paper mills nearby at South Carey Mill and West Mill at Wareham until 1817 and 1831.

The main paper-making centre was at Wimborne where the first site was established by 1700 at Buckets Mill, a former corn mill. Paper shipped to London in 1704 may have come from here and the Poole Town accounts of 1732 refer to George Rogers 'at ye paper mills at Wimborne'. A second paper mill at Canford Bridge was recorded in 1739. Isaac Taylor's Dorset map of 1765 shows a paper mill off Poole Road, Wimborne.

By 1780 Stephen Burt had been forced to move to a new site upstream at Witchampton (ST 999069) where there was less pollution in the River Allen. By 1851 this successful paper mill was using woodpulp and esparto grass and paper-making machinery included a 77-inch Fourdrinier machine. Ten years later William Burt was employing 62 workers and was joined by his son, also William. In 1889 Joseph Armfield replaced a waterwheel with a 40-inch diameter British Empire turbine of 45.6hp. Seven years later *The Miller* published a testimonial by William Burt stating how the turbine replaced:

… a very good breastshot waterwheel, and I find I have not only gained power but there is an advantage in being able to run without any trouble during floods … You fixed and started it in April 1889 and it has not cost me one shilling in repairs.

A private company was set up in 1924, and when it went public in 1947 the plant was said to comprise 'one of the most modern paper-making machines in this country'. The company specialised in wallpapers, box papers, photographic papers, blotting paper, cover paper and boards, and supplied well-known wallpaper and stationery manufacturers in Britain and abroad. The paper mill was closed in 1984 although it was reopened for a short period by former employees.

18

❧ MOVING TIMES: ROADS ❧

The Romans laid out the first properly engi-neered roads in Dorset and one of the best preserved stretches in England can be seen where the Ackling Dyke marches straight across Wyke Down on the high chalk of Cranborne Chase. Other Roman roads in Dorset have been ploughed out or are followed by modern roads, as seen westwards from Dorchester. For cen-turies, little attention was then paid to roads and their condition deteriorated. Parishes maintained their roads to a varying degree. The only lasting works of the medieval period are the river bridges, many of which still carry the weight of today's traffic.

Post routes passed through Dorset by the eigh-teenth century but it was not until the 1750s that the first major improvements began with the cre-ation of turnpike trusts. These were established by local landowners, merchants and others who wished to improve their roads to increase trade to benefit their town or district. An Act of Parliament gave authority to improve existing routes, build new ones and to maintain them. The trust was empowered to raise tolls to make a return on money invested and to pay for the works and maintenance. Each trust was renewed every twen-ty-one years or so and their renewal Acts often indicate the dates of changes and new routes.

The turnpike era saw 20 new trusts created in Dorset between 1752 and 1857, with short lengths of other trusts entering from neighbouring coun-ties. Few were ever a financial success and they were gradually extinguished, road maintenance passing to district authorities and then the coun-ty council in 1888. One lasting effect of the trusts was to fix the modern road system on the map of Dorset; routes that had been important in the past lost their status and even fell out of use if they were not turnpiked. Some sections of turnpike routes are now little more than country lanes, but others have become the main roads driven by motorists today. There were even bypasses. The A37 road at Charminster is a good example, and the route of the A350 through the village of Fontmell Magna was a new turnpike of the 1820s.

Roads in the chalk country were repaired with flints, but hammer-broken limestone was the preferred material elsewhere. Surfaces were generally good, but down in the clay vales of Blackmoor and the west, some minor roads were described by Stevenson in 1815 as 'miry, and

scarcely passable in winter, and the large rough stones with which they abound, render them very unpleasant in summer.'

Dorset's first turnpike was the Shaftesbury & Sherborne Trust, granted by an Act of 1752–3, fol-lowing the old Great Western Post Road along what is now the A30. The main route started in the east at Whitesheet Hill in Donhead St Andrew, Wiltshire, passed through Shaftesbury, Milborne Port and Sherborne to end at Halfway House towards Yeovil. There were radiating branches from Shaftesbury and Sherborne, and the trust was divided into two in 1778–79 for bet-ter administration. Records of the Sherborne Division at the Dorset Record Office tell of improvements, maintenance, the letting-out of toll-houses and a survey of their condition, and there was some conflict when the railways were being built around Sherborne. The second trust was the Harnham, Blandford & Dorchester Trust of 1753–54, which followed another post road from Salisbury to the west via Dorchester towards Bridport, now the A354 and A35.

By the end of the century there were 15 trusts, the most important of which included the Poole Trust (1755–56), the Bridport First and Second District Trusts (both 1764–65), Wareham Trust (1765–66) and the Maiden Newton Trust (1777–78). Their work in the early-nineteenth century involved making branches, realignments and completing links. The Blackmoor Vale Trust was active around Sturminster, for example, where *Pigot's Directory* for 1830 reported that:

> … a great benefit has lately been completed to the public, by making a new turnpike-road through the vale; the old parish roads being very narrow, and in winter almost impassable from the floods.

The Bridport First District Trust undertook major improvements on the Chideock to Charmouth section (now the A35), with new alignments and a tunnel at Thistle Hill, while the Bridport Second District Trust opened its own tunnel at Horn Hill in 1832. The five trusts created in the nineteenth century mostly linked other trusts. One of the last was the Puddletown & Wimborne Trust of 1840, but only seven years later the first railway was opened to Dorchester, taking away traffic, which caused financial loss to the road's chief promoter, J.S.W. Sawbridge Erle Drax of Charborough Park.

Nevertheless, this trust's legacy is the important link between Bere Regis and Wimborne that is followed today by the A31.

Physical features along the turnpike routes include engineering works involving cuttings, embankments and bridges, but many were altered or widened in later years and are passed today with hardly a glance. A good example of turnpike engineering survives at West Hill, Sherborne, where the Sherborne Trust south to Dorchester was rerouted in 1848 to form a curving climb at a steady gradient of 1 in 20 by the use of embankments and cuttings. This is still the A352, but the course of the original turnpike is seen in a field just to the west of the embankment at the foot of the hill *(ST 636156)*. Earlier, the same trust opened a much longer detour to the east of Milborne Port (in Somerset). The old route with a steep ascent can still be traced as a track, but the present A30 detours southwards towards Purse Caundle to make a steady climb up the escarpment of Toomer Hill. This added almost a mile to the route, which is reflected in alterations made to later mileposts along the road towards Shaftesbury.

Dorset's many bridges are an important aspect of the archaeology of roads. There are fine medieval stone arches, from the small Cornford Bridge *(ST 692120)*, built in about 1480 across the Caundle Brook in the Blackmoor Vale, to the magnificent twelfth-century White Mill Bridge *(ST 958005)* over the Stour. Bridges were repaired or widened over the years, although they remain narrow. The old arches can be seen beneath Sturminster Newton's Town Bridge *(ST 784136)* which was widened in 1820 and commemorated by a date stone set upside down on the central cutwater. Other historic bridges on the Stour and its tributaries include Crawford Bridge at Spetisbury and Julian's Bridge of 1636 at Wimborne.

Julian's Bridge at Wimborne was built in 1636 and widened in 1844 (note the brick under the arches) shortly after the Puddletown & Wimborne Trust opened a through route to Dorchester.

Bridges of the turnpike era were Blandford Bridge, built over an earlier one in 1783 and widened in 1812, and the three-arched Durweston Bridge of 1795. The latter was built to divert the old road away from the Bryanston Estate and has a slate plaque inscribed 'The Bridge was Built by Hen. W. Portman Esq An. Dom. 1795 Joseph Towsey Architect'. Greenstone was used at Durweston, but Canford Bridge at Wimborne was built of Portland stone in 1813 by John Dyson, engineer, and Jesse Bushrod, mason. These large bridges contrast with many smaller examples such as that inscribed 'County Bridge 1807' across Shreen Water in the centre of Gillingham.

Cast-iron notices on bridges of all ages are of particular interest as they include the well known warning:

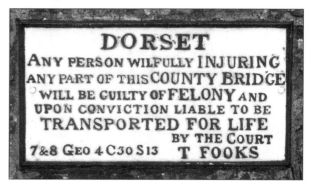

Transportation notice on Sturminster Bridge.

Fooks was Clerk of the Peace and the details of this Act of 1828 state that anyone convicted could be 'transported beyond the Seas for Life, or for any Term not exceeding Four Years; and, if a Male, to be once, twice, or thrice publicly or privately whipped (if the Court shall so think fit), in addition to such Imprisonment'. Some lost or stolen plates have been replaced with signs prefixed with 'Notice' instead of 'Dorset'. Later cast-iron warning plates of interest include one notice reflecting the times:

> County Council of Dorset. Take Notice that this Bridge (which is a County Bridge) is insufficient to carry weights beyond the ordinary traffic of the District; and that the owners and persons in charge of Locomotive Traction Engines and other ponderous Carriages are warned against using the bridge for the passage of any such Engine or Carriage. E. Archdall Ffooks. Clerk of the County Council of Dorset.

There were some iron road bridges of the industrial period and Bagber Bridge *(ST 764156)* across the River Lydden near Sturminster is of special note. It was built in about 1830 for the Blackmoor Vale Trust and has four cast-iron beams manufactured by the

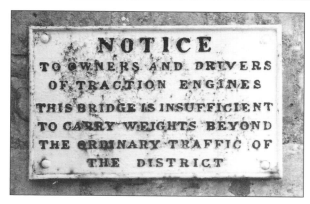

A bridge warning notice to traction engine drivers.

Tuckton Bridge is an early reinforced concrete bridge designed by Mouchel-Hennebique and was opened to carry Bournemouth trams in 1905. The attractive iron railings replaced the original concrete ones.

Bagber Bridge across the River Lydden in the Blackmoor Vale was made by the Coalbookdale Company.

Coalbrookdale Co. W. Dawes was the engineer and A. Collins the contractor. Wrought-iron ties underneath helped to strengthen the structure.

Lowest river crossing points were significant in the Weymouth and Poole areas. An important tideway bridge across Smallmouth Passage replaced an historic but inconvenient ferry and gave Portland its first direct connection to the mainland. An Act for a toll-bridge was passed in 1836 and a new timber trestle structure was opened on 30 January 1839. There were increasing problems with the timbers, and the bridge was shortened and rebuilt in 1867. It was replaced by an iron bridge in 1895–96 to the design of Sir John Coode, engineer of the breakwater, and this served Portland well until it was replaced by the present structure in 1985. A second bridge alongside carried a railway to Portland from 1864 to 1965.

Twentieth-century bridges include Tuckton Bridge, the lowest crossing on the Stour, which was opened in 1905 to replace a timber bridge of 1883. It is an early example of a reinforced concrete bridge, with 14 spans, and was built to carry the Bournemouth tram system to Christchurch. The three-arched concrete South Bridge at Wareham replaced a medieval bridge in 1927. Two lifting bridges were built to allow

Attention to detail: the arms of the Borough of Bournemouth in the centre of Tuckton Bridge.

vessels to navigate to the upper harbours at Poole (1927) and Weymouth (1930). Both bridges replaced earlier structures and are of special engineering interest. A 'temporary' bridge of the Second World War still carries traffic at Two Fords near Lydlinch. This is a 'Callender-Hamilton' galvanised steel structure, erected in 1942 by Canadian engineers alongside an older stone bridge. Another wartime connection is the more famous prefabricated military 'Bailey Bridge', invented by Sir Donald Bailey at Christchurch where a small section is displayed as a memorial in a park.

The lifting Town Bridge at Weymouth was completed in 1930, and replaced earlier bridges in the same vicinity.

This Callendar-Hamilton galvanised steel bridge was built during the Second World War at Two Fords at Lydlinch near Sturminster and still carries traffic on the A357. The more famous Bailey Bridge type was designed at Christchurch.

Horn Hill Tunnel, designed by Michael Lane, greatly improved communications between Beaminster and south Somerset when it was opened in 1832. A second road tunnel at Charmouth is no longer in use.

Two road tunnels in west Dorset are unusual for any county. The Horn Hill Tunnel (*ST 468032*) still takes traffic on the A3066 north of Beaminster. It was designed for the Bridport

Second District Trust by the young engineer Michael Lane, who had assisted Marc Brunel on the Thames Tunnel, to take the road 345 feet through the hill to avoid a steep and inconvenient climb. The route was an important link between the area around Crewkerne in south Somerset and Beaminster, Bridport and the harbour. Plaques over each portal, which are dangerous to read (!), state :

The Public are principally indebted for the erection of this TUNNEL to the zealous exertions of GILES RUSSELL of Beaminster, Gent. Begun August 1831. Finished June 1832. M. Lane, Civil Engineer.

An earthwork climbing the fields to the east of the tunnel indicates the course of the old road from Beaminster. The shorter Thistle Hill Tunnel (*ST 349949*) was opened in 1831 by the Bridport First District Trust to the northwest of Charmouth but has since been bypassed by the A35.

The iron footbridge at Sturminster Newton was built by J. Conway in 1841. The remains of the old Somerset & Dorset Railway bridge can be seen upstream.

River footbridges include a delightful example at Sturminster (*ST 783143*), an iron bridge erected by J. Conway in 1841 and the apparent namesake of Thomas Hardy's poem 'On Sturminster Foot-Bridge'. Further down the Stour, the late-nineteenth-century footbridge at Canford Magna (*SZ 030988*) is a narrow suspension bridge of 132-feet span between slender iron pillars. A second suspension bridge, designed and built by David Rowell & Co. in 1904, crosses Alum Chine in Bournemouth (*SZ 071905*). An early reinforced concrete footbridge of 1912 is nearby.

Toll-houses are the most recognisable legacy of the turnpike trusts, although many have disappeared. Typically, a toll-house had one or two storeys, with a bay protruding onto the roadside, opposite which stood the gate where the toll was paid to the keeper. A small side gate allowed pedestrians to pass through free. The position so close to roads busy with modern traffic has caused a number of toll-keepers' houses to be abandoned as dwellings and demolished, or others have been lost to road improvements. The Sherborne Trust's Whitepost toll-house *(ST 640193)* and the Maiden Newton Trust's two-storey Charminster toll-house *(SY 675921)* are among Dorset's finest, and there are further good examples of the Bridport First District Trust, such as at West Allington *(SY 456931)*. At Sherborne,

Lord Digby approved the plans of West Hill Toll-house, built in 1848 at the junction of the Dorchester and Blandford roads at the top of the newly graded climb from Sherborne.

White Post Toll-house is an attractive stone building at a crossroads to the north of Sherborne.

The toll-house beside the A37 at Charminster is one of the most conspicuous in Dorset. It was built in about 1840 by the Maiden Newton Trust on the new road to Dorchester.

A large toll-house of the Bridport First Division Trust at West Allington, Bridport.

West Hill toll-house *(ST 643145)* at the junction of the Dorchester and Blandford roads dates from the 1848 realignments, and its plans had first to be approved by Lord Digby of Sherborne Castle.

All houses displayed a prominent toll board and one of the Vale of Blackmoor Trust is still fixed to a toll-house at South Cheriton in Somerset *(ST 693248)*. By coincidence, three other toll boards of the 1820s from this same trust are preserved in Gillingham Museum (from Penns Mill and Madjeston) and the Salisbury & South Wiltshire Museum (New Cross Gate). They list the toll of 4½d:

> *… for every horse or beast drawing any Coach, Stagecoach, Berlin, Landau, Landaulet, Brouche, Chariot, Chaise, Chaise Marine, Calash, Curricle, Phaeton, Sociable, Gig, Chairm Car, caravan and van, Hearse, or Litter, or other such hired carriage…*

Such a lengthy description was obviously designed to prevent any possible evasion of the toll! Other charges were for commercial or farm vehicles (with a discount for wider and less-destructive wheels), and herded animals.

The turnpikes were required to erect milestones or mileposts. Standard milestones were carved with distances in Roman or other numerals between the nearest named towns, although Hyde Park Corner is included on stones near Wareham and at Blandford Forum. The stones had different shapes, with flat or rounded tops. A variation was to bolt on a cast-iron plate giving the details and there are examples of this type along the high road towards Sherborne from

Dorchester. A stone on the A37 outside Charminster (*SY 671929*) has a plate recording 2 miles from Dorchester 'by the new road', a clear reference to the bypass built by the Maiden Newton Trust after 1840.

Cast-iron mileposts were an alternative in the nineteenth century. Examples of these along the A30 to the east and west of Shaftesbury have a triangular shape but are hollow at the back. The two angled faces allow the details

Milestone and plate, 'Dorchester By The New Road', Charminster.

Milestone between Winterborne Abbas and Grimstone.

Milestone on A354 near Cashmore.

Milepost, Bristol Road, Sherborne.

Poole Trust Milepost between Wimborne and Cranborne.

Milepost in Salisbury Street, Shaftesbury, made by Cockey of Frome.

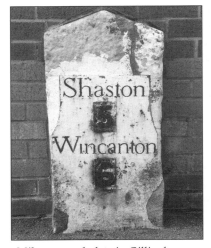

Milestone and plate in Gillingham.

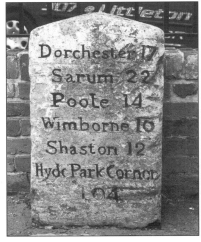

Milestone at Blandford, listing the important destinations.

Milestone near Wareham ('110 To Hyde Park Corner').

Milestone between Bere Regis and Wareham.

Milestone at Middlemarsh.

Milestone and plate between Dorchester and Sherborne.

A milestone's plate near Motcombe.

Poole/Wareham Trusts post at Lytchett Minster.

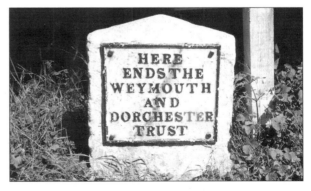

End of Weymouth & Dorchester Trust, Revels Hill.

to be read while still approaching and the name of the local parish is cast down the spine. They were made by Cockey of Frome some time in the mid-nineteenth century when they replaced the first milestones of the 1750s. A slightly different angled milepost used by the Poole Trust did not give the parish but were marked 'Poole Trust'. Good examples are seen on the B3078 from Wimborne to Cranborne, and elsewhere. Rectangular forms of mileposts with pediments stand at the approaches to Sherborne on the A30 and B3145.

The Poole Trust marked its meeting point with its neighbours, hence iron posts for the Poole/Blandford Trusts at *SY 949986* and the Poole/Wareham Trusts at *SY 955925*. At the foot of Revels Hill *(ST 676055)* a stone has a cast plate reading 'Here ends the Dorchester and Weymouth Trust'. To the north of this point the Sherborne Trust took over.

Most direction-posts or finger-posts in Dorset date from the twentieth century. Those with circular finials giving the location and grid reference were the brainchild of J.J. Leeming, county surveyor after the Second World War. Cast in aluminium, the first was set up at Hell Corner near Yetminster, followed by God's Blessing Green, near Wimborne. Other strange names are still to be

A typical post-war Dorset signpost finial giving the grid reference at Revels Hill. It disappeared soon after this photograph was taken in 2001.

found although they have increasingly been removed or lost. Occasionally a finger-post is cast with the maker's name, such as the Royal Label Factory of Stratford-upon-Avon at Perryfield Corner on Portland (*SY 695710*). The origin of three red-painted finger-posts in Dorset has caused much debate, with inconclusive suggestions ranging from the sites of gibbets, suicides, graves, markets or meeting places at parish boundaries and so on. In some instances they may have been intended to avoid confusion with nearby white posts (there is an example north of Sherborne).

Some examples of miscellaneous street furniture are drain covers, manhole covers, lamp standards, horse troughs, postboxes and telephone kiosks.

An iron water trough by Maggs of Bourton and fountain dated 1844 must have provided welcome refreshment to horses climbing the hill from Gillingham into Shaftesbury.

Working gas street lamps around Holdenhurst near Bournemouth are unusual survivals today.

As well as the bridge warnings described above, the county council saw fit to place other plates threatening to prosecute drivers of wagons or heavy vehicles for injuring the road surface 'by the improper use of a Skidpan, Dragshoe or otherwise'. Water troughs no longer serve their original purpose now that motor vehicles have replaced horse transport. They range from a cast-iron example by Maggs & Hindley at Enmore Green, Shaftesbury, to granite memorial troughs in Bournemouth.

Pillar or wall letter-boxes date from the mid-nineteenth century. The octagonal pillar-box with a vertical letter slot and weather flap at Barnes Cross near Holwell in the Blackmoor Vale is the oldest such in England still functioning at its original site *(ST 693117)*. It was made in 1853 by John M. Butt & Co. of the Kingsholme Ironworks, Gloucester. Another early pillar-box of the 1870s stands on the corner of South Walk and South Street in Dorchester. This is hexagonal with the top decorated with acanthus leaves and was designed by J.W. Penfold.

The postbox at lonely Barnes Cross in the Blackmoor Vale dates from 1853 and is the oldest still in use in England.

This delightful Penfold-designed postbox is at the corner of South Walks and South Street in Dorchester.

Telephone kiosks became familiar street items in the twentieth century. A very rare example of the first standard design introduced in 1921, the Kiosk No.1, can be seen at Tyneham, Purbeck. It has survived here ever since the village was taken over by the War Department in the Second World War. It is of concrete beneath an ornate roof. The Kiosk No.6 was the most famous and familiar design, designed by Sir Giles Gilbert Scott in King George V's silver jubilee year. Since the 1980s many of these have been replaced by modern designs.

The closest Dorset came to the canal age was the ill-fated Dorset & Somerset Canal of the 1790s which was intended to bring Somerset coal into the county. Only sections of a branch in Somerset were ever built, although its course through the Blackmoor Vale to the River Stour near Shillingstone was still marked on a map of Dorset by Thomas Dix published in 1820. Even ten years later, *Pigot's Directory* was describing Stalbridge as being 'situated on a branch of the River Stour and the Dorsetshire and Somersetshire canal'. Dorset, though, had to be content with its roads until the promotion of railways.

The lost village of Tyneham has a rare early No.1 design of telephone kiosk.

19

❧ RAILWAYS AND TRAMWAYS ❧

The earliest railways in Dorset were built for minerals, the first in 1806 for Purbeck ball clay and the second twenty years later for Portland stone. Despite proposals for a Radstock, Shaftesbury & Poole Railway in 1825, and a line between Dorchester and Weymouth in 1834, it was not until 1847 that the first mainline passenger railway was opened into Dorset. The subsequent railway developments have been widely published and a summary will suffice.

Dorset's four main railway routes were all promoted and opened within sixteen years, with two from east to west and two from north to south. These were the Southampton & Dorchester Railway (1847), Wiltshire, Somerset & Weymouth Railway (1857), Salisbury & Yeovil Railway (1859–60), and the Somerset & Dorset Joint Railway (1860–63). It was then a matter of filling in the gaps, by adding branches or making alterations and connections, most particularly in the Poole and Bournemouth area. The main network was virtually complete by the early-twentieth century, but the railways that served Dorset well could not compete against the advent of motor cars, lorries and coaches on

the roads. The system was pared down in the 1960s with one major closure (the S & DJR), track singling and branch closures, the last in 1975. Steam trains operated until 1967.

The two east–west routes were promoted by the London & South Western Railway, and in 1847 the Southampton & Dorchester Railway was opened from Ringwood and thence through Wimborne and Wareham to a terminus at Dorchester, from which it was intended to press on further west. There was a short branch from Poole Junction to the first station for Poole at Hamworthy. This railway's rather circuitous route into the county earned it the nickname 'Castleman's Corkscrew', after the Wimborne solicitor and main promoter Charles Castleman. Railway developments around Poole and Bournemouth were complex. Poole gained a town station in 1874 but the exclusive Bournemouth was satisfied with stations to the east and west before a central station was built in 1885, three years before the direct line from Southampton to Dorchester finally replaced the old 'Corkscrew' route.

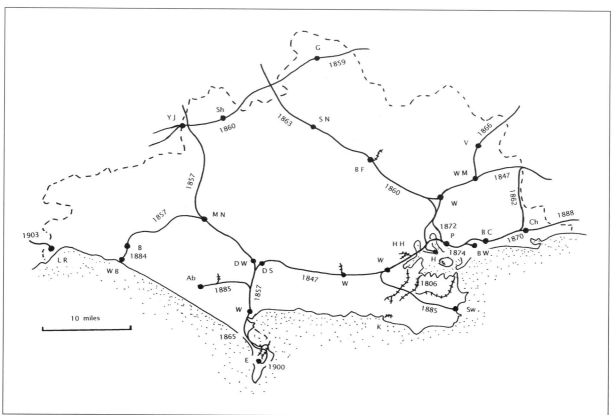

A map of Dorset's railways.

The second LSWR line was the Salisbury & Yeovil Railway which was opened through north Dorset in 1859–60, with stations at Gillingham, Sherborne and Yeovil Junction. This was, and remains, the main line from Waterloo to Exeter. The first sod was cut amid great ceremony in a field near Gillingham by Miss Seymour, sister of the company's chairman, on 3 April 1856. The commemorative silver spade and ornate walnut wood wheelbarrow are preserved in Gillingham Museum.

The rival Great Western Railway had opened the broad-gauge Wiltshire, Somerset & Weymouth Railway down through Yeovil to Dorchester and Weymouth in 1857. Residents of Weymouth and Dorchester could now enjoy a choice of routes to London, arriving at either Paddington or Waterloo. The final length from Dorchester to Weymouth was shared as a mixed-gauge line with the LSWR. It was converted to standard gauge in 1874 and, although now mostly single track and with reduced stations, this line is still in operation.

A second north–south route was the Somerset & Dorset Joint Railway, which was an amalgamation of the Dorset Central from Wimborne to Blandford (1860) and the Somerset Central through to Sturminster, Stalbridge and beyond (1863). This much-loved line gave access to Bournemouth for holiday traffic from the Midlands. It was closed in 1966, although freight was carried between Wimborne and Blandford for another three years.

Dorset's first branch line was the Bridport Railway, promoted by the people of that town. It was opened from the WSWR at Maiden Newton in 1857. It was broad gauge until 1874 and was bought by the Great Western in 1901. There were intermediate stations at Toller and Powerstock, and in 1884 the line was extended from Bridport to promote a potential resort around the renamed West Bay harbour. This section, however, closed to passengers in 1930 and goods in 1966 but the remainder survived until 1975.

In the east, a branch was opened in 1862 from the LSWR near Ringwood to Christchurch (then in Hampshire), while in 1866 the Salisbury & Dorset Junction Railway branched off at West Moors to Verwood and thence to Fordingbridge and Downton before joining the main line near Salisbury. In 1865 the Weymouth & Portland Railway was a branch from Weymouth to Chiswell on Portland. A branch ran into the naval base after 1876 but it was not until 1900 that the Easton & Church Hope Railway was extended through the landslips of East Weare to the top of the island. Closure came in 1965.

The Abbotsbury Railway (1885–1952) was a short-lived branch with little passenger or goods traffic, despite a promising start with quarries at Portesham. There were no major works but construction took six years because of financial problems. The year 1885 also saw the opening of the Swanage Railway from Wareham which carried rising numbers of holiday-makers, as well as stone and clay traffic. The Furzebrook to Swanage section was closed in 1972, but the track has since been relaid. The Lyme Regis Railway was the last branch in Dorset, opened in 1903 from Axminster in Devon, through which county most of the line passed.

The railways had a major impact on the landscape through which they were cut. Since closure, parts have been erased while other sections have left more positive traces. Whether working or abandoned, the archaeology of railways includes engineering works such as cuttings, embankments, bridges, tunnels and stations. A typical small rural railway station included a platform, station building incorporating a booking hall and waiting rooms, and perhaps a platform canopy. With double track, a second platform had lesser accommodation and was approached by a footbridge. A stationmaster's house, signal box and water tower might complete the scene. A station yard gave vehicular approach and a nearby hotel was convenient for commercial travellers. There might also be short sidings and a goods yard with buildings, serving the immediate rural area.

Bournemouth Station has an impressive façade and glazed roof, recently saved by a restoration project.

Bournemouth Central *(SZ 097919)* is the largest and most impressive station in Dorset. Opened by the LSWR in 1885 as Bournemouth East and recently refurbished, it is a splendid buttressed brick structure supporting an iron-arched glass roof. Christchurch Station *(SZ 153932)* was opened in 1886 and has canopies on both platforms supported by decorative cast-iron work. Wareham Station *(SY 920881)* dates from the same period and also has platform canopies supported

Attractive ironwork supports the roof canopy on the down platform at Christchurch Station, opened in 1886.

Wareham Station was rebuilt in 1886 following the opening of the branch to Swanage and remains a good example of LSWR architecture.

The London & South Western Railway's coat of arms at Wareham Station.

by cast-iron pillars. It was completely rebuilt following the opening of the branch to Swanage. The brick and stone building under a tiled roof has the LSWR's coat of arms and a date of 1886, although it was not officially opened until the following April. A brick goods shed associated with the first station stands derelict. Further west, the original stations at Dorchester South and Weymouth have been replaced.

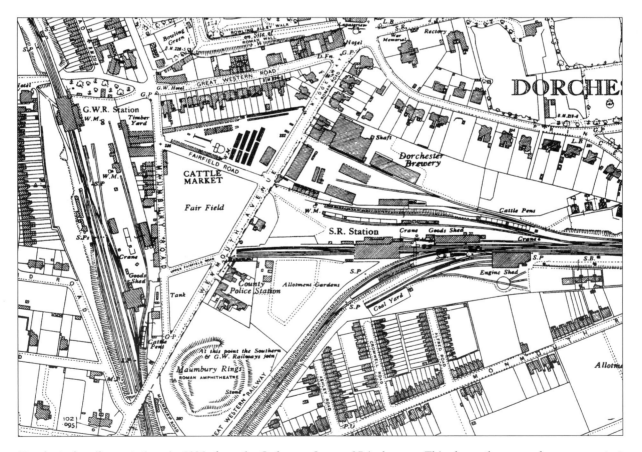

Dorchester's railway stations in 1928, from the Ordnance Survey 25-inch map. This shows the unusual arrangement at Dorchester South, where the original LSWR station was on a line planned to continue west. Trains were obliged to reverse in and out of here before platforms were built on the Weymouth curve. Note also the sidings here and at the GWR's covered Dorchester West Station. Both railway lines carefully avoid the ancient earthwork of Maumbury Rings.

On the old WSWR, Dorchester West Station was originally covered with a wooden roof. The station building, no longer in use by the railway, was designed by Ritson and has Italianate window openings. Maiden Newton *(SY 599980)* is a typical country station with a knapped flint and Ham stone building (now offices) and the bay for the Bridport branch. In north Dorset, the tall slate-hung station building at Gillingham *(ST 810261)* was designed by Sir William Tite. Opposite, the South Western Commercial Hotel and Posting House was built some years after the railway. Sidings once served the town and the brickworks. Sherborne Station *(ST 641162)* was also designed by Tite in stone and includes the stationmaster's house. The footbridge dates from 1886. The S & DJR route is one of the more interesting of the closed lines. The only remaining station at Shillingstone *(ST 824117)* is a good example of a small rural station building in brick and stone with a slate roof and large canopy. Both platforms survive but the goods yard became an industrial estate. At Blandford, the station site has been built over, although the iron footbridge remains and the cutting to the north is a pathway.

Maiden Newton at the junction with the Bridport branch has a typical country station building in knapped flint with Ham stone details.

No rails, but still standing. There are plans to restore Shillingstone Station on the old Somerset & Dorset Railway.

Only an iron footbridge survives as a reminder of the site of Blandford Station.

The Abbotsbury branch railway has surviving station and goods buildings of stone. The Broadwey Station building and goods shed have been put to other uses, the station at Portesham is now a house, while only the goods shed survives at Abbotsbury. The only major structure along the route is a tall stone bridge across a lane at Upwey. The Bridport Railway's Powerstock Station has been converted to a house, but only the platform survives at Toller. Both Bridport's stations have gone, but West Bay Station *(SY 465904)*, last used for passengers in 1930, has been restored and a short length of track laid by the platform. This delightful little building has tall chimneys and iron canopy supports cast with 'BR', and fully deserves its preservation. The contrast between this and Bournemouth could hardly be greater.

West Bay Station was opened in 1884 when the Bridport Railway was extended to the harbour in an attempt to develop tourism. It closed to passengers in 1930 but this charming little building has now been restored. The canopy once extended to the platform edge.

The Swanage terminus station (*SZ 029789*) was built of local stone in 1885 when the branch opened, and was extended in 1938. This atmospheric station escaped destruction when the line closed in 1972 and has since been preserved by the Swanage Railway group. Although the goods yard has gone, the engine shed, turntable and coaling point survive intact on this working steam railway. The branch's other fine station, at Corfe Castle (*SY 962821*), has also been saved and brought back into use.

Two redundant station buildings are preserved outside Dorset. Nine years after closure in 1965, the wooden station building at Lyme Regis was dismantled and re-erected as a shop at Alresford Station on the Watercress Line in Hampshire. Another wooden station building, erected at Toller on the Bridport branch in 1905, found its way to the South Devon Railway at Totnes in Devon.

Stone or brick bridges over or under railways abound, but the most spectacular was built to

A busy steam railway terminus has been recreated at Swanage.

The Swanage engine shed, turntable and coaling point are once more in use for steam locomotives. The main difference between today and the past is that the opening to the engine shed was originally arched.

Corfe Castle has a perfect example of a late-Victorian station, once more in use by steam trains.

The most elaborate bridge in Dorset carried the Southampton & Dorchester Railway over the private driveway to Canford House.

Abandoned railway: this bridge over the old Somerset & Dorset Railway at King's Mill Lane, near Stalbridge, has since been removed for the benefit of road traffic. Similar traces of the railway age are gradually disappearing from the landscape.

take a private driveway from Canford Manor under the original Southampton & Dorchester line near Wimborne *(SU 019990)*. This is a highly ornate structure built of freestone embellished with heraldry on both sides. Of the few iron bridges, one carrying a road over the LSWR at Gillingham retained the original iron spans cast with 'Brymbo 1858' until it was replaced in 1991. The Somerset & Dorset Railway crossed the Stour four times on lattice bridges between Sturminster

and Blandford. The ironwork was removed after the railway closed, leaving behind the brick and stone approaches.

Dorset has few viaducts and the most striking are the two brick and stone spans at Bourne Valley, Branksome *(SZ 062922)*, built in 1885 as part of the link between Poole and Bournemouth. The western viaduct still carries the main line but the other viaduct, or Gasworks Curve, to the old

The Bourne Valley viaducts at Branksome were completed in 1885 as part of the railway improvements around Bournemouth.

The 'cut and cover' tunnel at Frampton, seen from a road bridge to the west.

The short but solid viaduct at Grimstone was designed by Brunel for the Wiltshire, Somerset & Weymouth Railway.

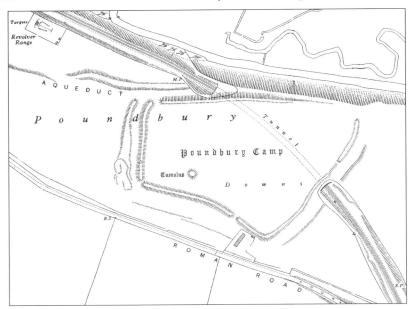

Poundbury Tunnel at Dorchester, from the Ordnance Survey 25-inch map. Protests by William Barnes and others led Brunel and his engineers to route their railway beneath the Iron-Age fort at Poundbury instead of making a cutting. The Roman aqueduct is also seen between the railway and the hillfort.

ORDNANCE SURVEY: CROWN COPYRIGHT RESERVED

Bournemouth West Station is disused. A solid three-arched viaduct at Grimstone *(SY 640945)* was designed by Brunel for the WSWR. It has a main central arch over the lane to Sydling St Nicholas and two lesser side arches, one taking the stream of Sydling Water. The two main piers each have four minor arches. A short stone viaduct on the Swanage branch is conspicuous in the shadow of Corfe Castle, and there is a smaller viaduct at Eccliffe on the Yeovil line just west of Gillingham. Also of note are the Holes Bay Viaduct and the arched Rockley Viaduct crossing tidal creeks at Poole and Hamworthy.

Four tunnels were built by the WSWR, at Holywell on the summit level and Frampton, Poundbury and Bincombe. The 660-yard Frampton Tunnel *(SY 631951)* is a good example of a 'cut and cover' tunnel to save the landowner's property from being dissected by a continuous cutting. There could have been a cutting at Poundbury just outside Dorchester, but Brunel and the railway company were persuaded to avoid destroying part of the hillfort by driving a 264-yard tunnel. This was an early example of conservation led by William Barnes and the Dorset County Museum. Bincombe Tunnel *(SY 673856)* cuts through the chalk ridgeway between Dorchester and Weymouth. It is 814 yards long and stone-arched portals are approached at both ends through deep cuttings. Dorset's second longest tunnel was completed in February 1860 at Buckhorn Weston to the west of Gillingham *(ST 773247)*. The difficult geology of the Kimmeridge

The Bincombe Tunnel cuts deep beneath the chalk ridgeway between Dorchester and Weymouth and is the longest in Dorset. A mixed broad and standard gauge ran through here from 1857 until 1874.

clay caused problems with water and the tunnel's length of 739 yards was expensively lined with over six million bricks.

Technology had advanced by 1884 when a steam navvy was used for excavating the long cutting to the north of Meyrick Park in Bournemouth, where much of the spoil was deposited in the embankment approaching the Bourne Valley viaducts. It is difficult to visualise today how only manpower was employed for all construction work on embankments and cuttings on the early railway routes.

While the major railways had an impact on Dorset's trade and the mobility of people, its humbler mineral railways and tramways were no less important to the county's economy. The first of these highly individual lines was constructed in the early part of 1806 by Benjamin Fayle, who revolutionised the transport of ball clay from his Norden pits to a shipping place at Middlebere on a southern creek of Poole Harbour. The Middlebere Tramway was named as 'Iron Rail Way' on the first one-inch Ordnance Survey map of 1811, which indicated two passing places along its course, and a third at the quay. A branch ran into two clay pits to the east of the turnpike near Norden and carried on beneath the road. The 3½-mile tramway was a plateway of 3-feet 9-inches gauge. In 1815 Stevenson described the L-shaped iron plateway rails as 3-feet long, ⅝-

inch thick at the bottom, with a 3½-inch-wide plate and 3-inch-high edging next to the horse path between the sleeper blocks. Each rail weighed about 40lb and the ends had a small recess to take a large-headed nail driven into an oak-plugged hole in a stone sleeper block. The wagons carried 2 tons of clay and three horses drew 10 tons down to the quay three times daily at a cost of about 6d per ton. Fayle's tramway closed in about 1905 when clay was then carried to Goathorn Pier. The route across Hartland Moor has a shallow cutting and an embankment where a few stone sleeper blocks remain in the track bed *(SY 961851)*. Two tunnels run close together beneath the Wareham to Corfe road. The south portal of the earliest tunnel *(SY 948832)* has a keystone inscribed 'BF 1807', which makes this a very early date for a rail tunnel. A stone dated 1848 over the second tunnel portal may refer to repair work.

The line of Fayle's Middlebere Tramway curves through a cutting on Hartland Moor.

A plateway sleeper block of the Middlebere Tramway, with a drilled hole to take an oak plug and iron nail. A 50-pence coin provides a scale.

The south portal of Benjamin Fayle's original tramway tunnel at Norden has a keystone inscribed 'BF 1807'.

It was not until 1840 that another clay railway was built, this time running straight across Stoborough Heath for 2 miles from Furzebrook to Ridge Wharf on a bend of the River Frome below Wareham. Loaded clay wagons descended by gravity but horses pulled back the empties and worked in the sidings. The railway was relaid at 2-foot 8½-inch gauge in 1866 for working by steam locomotives and it became the policy of Pike Brothers to name each of their new locomotives numerically from 'Primus' to 'Septimus', this last in 1930. The railway was diverted onto Creech Heath to serve new clay pits and mines as they were developed away to the southwest, finally extending for over 2 miles. The line to Ridge closed in 1943 and the upper section of the Pike railway continued in use until 1957. The locomotive 'Secundus' was later displayed at the Birmingham Museum of Science & Industry in the city where it had been built in 1874 by Bellis & Seekings. Although of light construction, parts of the railway's course are still clear, such as where it crosses the Arne road *(SY 937863)* or a lane at Grange Gate *(SY 917831)*. Engine sheds survive at Ridge and Furzebrook.

When Fayle & Co. developed clay pits at Newton Heath they built a tramway in the 1860s to a pier at the end of the Goathorn peninsula. This 3-feet 9-inch gauge Goathorn Railway was extended in 1905 to serve the Norden clay works, making the old Middlebere Tramway redundant. One of the line's steam locomotives was the 'Tiny' which was manufactured by Stephen Lewin of Poole. The line was closed in about 1936 when sidings at Norden served the Swanage Railway. Some of the line between the clay pits and works at Norden survived, crossing the main Corfe road until 1970. It was relaid at 1-foot 11½-inch gauge in 1948 and the steam locomotive 'Russell' of 1906 worked here briefly before it was replaced by small diesel locomotives.

The Swanage Pier Tramway of 1859 was fully revealed during renovation work along the sea front in 1994.

M. DOLAMORE

These were the main mineral railways in Purbeck, but shorter lines included a tramway opened in the 1850s on Brownsea Island where it ran between clay pits, a brick and pipe works and a shipping pier. The Swanage Pier Railway was opened along the sea front in 1859 to carry stone kerbs, setts and paving from the stone bankers to the new shipping pier. John Mowlem and George Burt were two of the instigators of this tramway and the pier which greatly improved the facilities for exporting Purbeck stone until the Swanage Railway arrived in the town in 1885. Although long closed, the rails still survive in places along the sea front *(SZ 033787)*. In the late-nineteenth century there was a short inclined tramway down the north side of the high ridge at Cocknowle *(SY 933821)*. Chalk and marl pits were opened up along the ridge and the product was sent down the incline to be loaded into road wagons at the bottom and carried to Thomas Powell's cement works at Ridge. Tramways served shipping piers at Kimmeridge during different attempts to exploit the shale from the cliffs. The first was opened by the Bituminous Shale Co. in 1848 from their clifftop diggings at Cuddle, and its faint course can be discerned contouring the hillside below Clavel's Tower. A short tramway ran from adit and cliff workings onto an iron jetty at Clavell's Hard from 1858–60, and in the last workings of 1883–90, a mile-long tramway ran down to a timber pier at Kimmeridge.

Portland had the greatest concentration of railways anywhere in Dorset, with an incredible 13 miles or more of quarry tramways crammed into the tiny island in the early-1900s. Exports of Portland stone were hindered by poor land carriage down steep hills to the shipping places, so in 1826 the Portland Railway Co. constructed a railway down to Castletown Pier via an incline from Priory Corner, to which stone was brought by road or tramway branches. This new railway encouraged quarry developments on the north

end of the island and ten years later it carried 32,315 tons of stone. It was of 4-foot 6-inch gauge and horses worked the upper section around the side of the Verne to a winding drum at the head of the long inclined plane. From here, loaded wagons descended on a cable while empties were drawn back up.

The Portland, or Merchants' Railway had carried thousands of tons of stone before it closed in October 1939. It never reopened after the war and the rails were lifted in 1957, but much remains to be seen on Portland. From the top of the incline (SY 689738) the courses of two lines with sleeper blocks can be followed around the Verne to the

Stone bridges and incline at a crossing of two branches of the Merchants' Railway at Verne Yeates, Portland. Four bridges were built here from 1875 to 1882.

This arch dated 1866 was for a tramway beneath Wide Street from Tout Quarry into Inmosthay Quarry, Portland.

head of a valley from where the main route continues to Priory Corner, with an inclined branch into the Waycroft Quarries. The higher route crosses this to turn through a cutting into the same quarries. This complex arrangement, with the addition of two roads, required four bridges (all with date stones from 1875 to 1882) and an incline at *SY 692733*. A third branch, now infilled, ran from Verne Yeates into Kingbarrow Quarries. Priory Corner and the site of the crane have been lost to road improvements, but sleeper blocks of branches can be followed in Tout Quarry, where they once continued through tunnels beneath Wide Street into Inmosthay Quarry. At its peak the quarry firms also had extensive railway branches into Withies Croft and Independent Quarries. F.J. Barnes had an independent 2-foot gauge line with the steam locomotive 'Excelsior' for taking waste for tipping at West Cliff in 1898.

The Admiralty or Breakwater Railway was opened in 1847 for the purposes of building Portland Breakwater. It descended the northeast side of Portland by an incline in three stages, each with a winding drum. There were branches into the convict and Admiralty Quarries and the loaded wagons carried stone out on timber trestles onto the breakwater construction site. It was used again at the turn of the century for the second breakwater works, when stone was loaded into barges in the dockyard. Steam locomotives worked the upper part of the railway. After it was abandoned, a road was built along the course of the incline.

Military railways included branches into the naval dockyard at Portland, miles of standard and narrow-gauge track in the RN Cordite Factory at Holton Heath and branches laid in the First World War to serve Bovington Camp and Blandford Camp, as noted in Chapter 24.

The military railway branch to Blandford Camp, in its last days in April 1922. The Blandford Brewery chimney is seen in the distance. Taken to show a geological feature in the cutting, this photograph captured a rare view of the short-lived line.

BRITISH GEOLOGICAL SURVEY (NERC COPYRIGHT RESERVED)

20

❧ PORTS AND SHIPPING ❧

Dorset's coastline offered opportunities for trade where there was access to the sea, and the two sheltered natural harbours of Poole and Weymouth flourished as ports in the Middle Ages. Lyme Regis and Bridport were also significant, the former protected by an artificial breakwater. Portland Roads provided an anchorage between Portland and Chesil Beach long before there was a dockyard at Castletown. Fishing, however, was carried out at many places, often directly from the beach such as at Portland where the 'lerret' was designed to be launched from the steep Chesil Beach.

Lyme Regis has an early example of an artificial harbour, which may date from around the fourteenth century when it was the second port in Dorset. Erosion of the cliffs on either side has left the harbour some distance from the shore. The protecting breakwater known as the Cobb was described by Defoe in the 1720s as a:

> … massy pile of building … consisting of one main and solid wall of stone, large enough for carts and carriages to pass on the top, and to admit houses and ware houses to be built upon it.

The Cobb's curving outer breakwater, originally built of local Lias limestone, was much repaired in Portland stone after damaging storms.

Captain Robert D'Arcy used iron cramps to hold the stones together during repairs in 1792–93, and after a major breach it was last repaired under the direction of Lt Col Fanshaw, Royal Engineers, in 1825–26. The tough shelly Portland Roach is shown to good effect in the stone blocks of the Cobb. It gives protection to the Landing Wharf or Victoria Pier, where a scale of harbour dues of 1879 is preserved on an old warehouse wall. The last coasting vessels called in 1939.

Bridport Harbour acquired the name West Bay in the 1880s during attempts to develop the place as a resort served by the new railway. There was some sort of port here at the mouth of the Brit since at least the thirteenth century, but its

Lyme Regis Harbour is protected by the Cobb.

The Danish steamship Nerma *in the harbour at West Bay, c.1900. This ship, built in 1893 and owned by J. Lauritzen, visited West Bay several times. For example, she brought a cargo of hemp from Riga for William Hounsell & Co. in May 1901. Note the salt house on the left and the undeveloped land behind.*

entrance was frequently blocked by the movement of sand and shingle at the west end of Chesil Beach. Defoe reported no harbour in the 1720s but from 1740–44 the engineer John Reynolds built two entrance piers through the shingle to a harbour which was scoured with water controlled by sluices. Further improvements were made by the civil engineer Francis Giles from 1823–25 and trade flourished, with over 500 ships calling in 1830. Hemp and flax from Russia, timber from Scandinavia, and coal from Wales and northeast England were imported, while beach gravel was exported. Shipbuilding took place on the west side of the harbour until about 1880. The narrow entrance was never easy for shipping and trade was lost to the railway. The storm-damaged west pier was repaired in 1857 to the designs of John Coode, who was supervising the Portland Breakwater works at the time. The last small ships called with timber in the 1960s and the L-shaped harbour basin is used for fishing and pleasure craft. Warehouses and a salt house have been converted to other uses.

The narrow harbour at Weymouth turns north into the Backwater and thence to Radipole Lake, perhaps where Roman vessels once berthed. Weymouth became a cross-Channel ferry port in 1794 when the Post Office introduced a weekly packet service to the Channel Islands, later increased to twice weekly. Steamships appeared on the run in the 1820s, but the service moved to Southampton in 1845. However, after the railway arrived in 1857 the LSWR and the rival Channel Islands Steam Packet Co. Ltd ran steamer services, although the former's vessel was wrecked in 1859. The GWR ran a service to Cherbourg from 1878–85. The pier on the north side of the harbour was lengthened in 1860. The Weymouth Harbour Tramway (worked by horses until 1880) was opened from Weymouth Station in 1865 and extended in 1889 to the GWR's new landing stage and baggage hall, built when three large steamers were introduced to rival the LSWR's Southampton service. Although the harbour tramway has closed, the rails through the streets to the quay survive. By 1960 Weymouth was the main port for the Channel Islands, but it was losing out to larger cross-Channel ports on the south coast. Redevelopments in the early-1970s changed the port to a drive-on car service to the Channel Islands and Cherbourg.

Few large vessels entered the Backwater, at the end of which Sir John Coode designed a dam to control flooding in 1872 as part of a sewage scheme that was never fully completed. Water was later controlled by sluices at the Westham Embankment and part of the Backwater was reclaimed in the 1920s. Warehouses, since converted to other uses, can be seen along the north side of the harbour, where the fish and ice store of 1855 is of Portland stone beneath a wide canopied roof. Cosens & Co.'s engineering and ship repairing

West Bay is now a place for small fishing and pleasure boats, but it was once busy with imports, exports and shipbuilding, and some warehouses remain. Pier Terrace on the right was built in 1885 in an attempt to develop West Bay as a resort.

Weymouth's fish house and ice store is built of Portland stone beneath slate roofing.

of loading ships was laborious. The stones were taken on a large-wheeled cart out into the water as far as possible with a horse, then manhandled into a rowing barge and taken out to deep water to be transshipped again into a waiting sailing vessel. There was a small stone quay but in 1859 the Swanage Pier & Tramway Co. built a timber pier for shipping stone and importing coal. Easterly winds made the use of this exposed pier difficult and it was poorly maintained by the time the railway took away its trade in 1885. The New Pier was built with a double deck from 1893–95 for use by passenger paddle-steamers. Like the earlier pier, it became derelict but has been rescued and restored by the Swanage Pier Trust.

establishment was on Commercial Road beside the Backwater, but the site was demolished in 1988. They also ran an ice-making factory in 1925–64 and had two slipways on the south side of the harbour. Cosens & Co. were best known for their fleet of paddle-steamers between 1848 and 1966, offering excursions to Lulworth Cove (where they landed on the beach), Swanage, Bournemouth, the Isle of Wight, Lyme Regis or Torquay.

Swanage was shipping Purbeck stone for centuries before it emerged as a tourist resort in Victorian times. Large quantities of stone kerbs, setts and paving slabs awaiting shipment were stored in 'bankers' along the shore. The traditional method

In the 1720s Defoe found Poole 'a considerable sea-port, and indeed the most considerable in all this part of England.' Poole was closely involved with the Newfoundland fishery and carried on commercial trade too, with imports of coal from northeast England. Over 200 sailing vessels were involved in coastwise trade and the Newfoundland fishery in 1815 and most foreign trade was carried on at Poole. Exports were provisions, nets, cordage, sailcloth, pipe clay and malt, and imports included cod, salmon, seal skins and fur. The fishery declined, however, and Poole's prosperity as a port suffered in the early-nineteenth century. Coal and timber continued to be imported, shipbuilding took place at Hamworthy, and efforts were made to improve the harbour.

Cosens & Co.'s paddle-steamer Victoria *arrives at Lulworth Cove and is manoeuvring into the shore while men are wheeling out the mobile landing stage on the beach. Built in 1884, this vessel was not scrapped until 1953.*

The New Pier at Swanage was opened in 1895 for paddle-steamer traffic and has been recently refurbished. The timber piles of the first stone pier of 1859 are seen in the foreground.

The main quay, which once had a railway, is now busy with tourist attractions but there are still hints of the warehouses behind the frontages. The Waterfront Museum is in the former Oakley Brothers' warehouse of 1877, which has fine exteriors with five floors and attic hoists. The adjacent fifteenth-century woolhouse known as the Town Cellars now houses the Local Studies Centre. Notable early-nineteenth-century buildings include the Customs House (1813) and Harbour Office (1822). Across the lifting Poole Bridge (1927) are Lower Hamworthy and the Ballast Quay where most commercial shipping calls, including vessels to load Purbeck ball clay for export. Twentieth-century travelling cranes for discharging coal here and at the gasworks' quay have now gone. There are also repair yards and a new ferry port on reclaimed land.

Poole's Custom House of 1813, with the fifteenth-century Town Cellars and Oakleys' tall warehouse of 1877, now housing the Waterfront Museum.

Iron bollard and granite coping at the eastern extension of Poole Quay. Very few such fixtures and details remain in Dorset's ports.

At the mouth of Poole Harbour, the Sandbanks chain ferry or floating bridge was established in July 1926 by the Bournemouth-Swanage Motor Road & Ferry Co. A new road was built along the Studland peninsula, with a slipway at the end, facing another at Sandbanks on the Poole side.

The steam-powered *Ferry No.1* was built by J. Samuel White on the Isle of Wight and could carry 15 cars. After the war years, this ferry was replaced during refits by a much smaller steam ferry which had served between East and West Cowes. *Ferry No.3* was built locally in 1959 by J. Bolson & Son at Poole and was powered by diesel engines. It was much larger and could carry 28 cars, dimensions being 157-feet long and 42-feet wide. After many years of reliable service, the current ferry was introduced in 1994, with a capacity of 48 cars.

Dorset's mineral wealth could not have been exploited without the building of small shipping places, all now abandoned and ruinous but of great interest. Some of the remarkable places for shipping stone off the Purbeck cliffs have been described above. These were mostly rocky ledges that suited the purpose during calm seas. On Portland's east coast, King's Pier, Folly Pier and Durdle Pier were built beneath the landslips of East Weare in the seventeenth and eighteenth centuries for the export of stone to London. Storm damage was frequent and little survives. Stone blocks still awaiting shipment are lined up on the slope leading down to Durdle Pier (*SY 705717*) where a timber derrick is now used for launching and landing small open fishing boats. A sea-corroded iron hand-winch on the crane is cast with the maker's name, Galpin of Dorchester.

Towards the Bill natural ledges were adapted to make shipping places; their cranes were vulnerable to the elements and were no doubt replaced several times. The foundations of vanished cranes can be found. Visiting the busy stone quarries at Portland Bill in 1855, Walter White described:

> *At one place, where vessels may lie in deep water close to the shore, stands a powerful crane; but only in calm weather can such an exposed shipping-wharf be made available.*

This is probably the site of the iron derrick now used for boat launching, but surrounded by traces of earlier cranes. An older timber derrick at Sandholes (*SY 687692*) may be the original stone loading crane, with iron winding gear made by Isles Ltd of the Steam Crane Works, Stanningley, near Leeds. The west coast of Portland is more exposed but a pier was constructed below the West Weare where shipping was extremely difficult.

Cliff crane near Portland Bill where stone was once loaded into boats. Note the squared blocks that were never shipped. This iron crane has replaced several previous ones over the years. It is now used for launching small fishing boats.

From 1826, the Merchants' Railway facilitated the shipment of very large tonnages of stone at Castletown Pier (SY 687744) where sidings ran out to at least 11 different merchants' shipping places in 1848. Some stone was still shipped after the railway closed in 1939. Despite alterations, large stone blocks in the construction of Castletown Pier tell of its original purpose.

Now reduced to a small fishing cove and slipway, Kimmeridge (SY 909788) had a series of piers built ever since the early-seventeenth century when Sir William Clavell established short-lived alum, glass- and salt-works. His pier was said to be 100-feet long, 60-feet wide and 50-feet high. Later piers were built to serve the shale industry and their stone foundations among the rocks at low tide are best observed from the cliff top above. The most prominent ruin is a sloping breakwater built in 1860 as part of Wanostrocht & Co.'s shale developments. Some timbers and iron

Hopes were high for a prosperous shale industry in 1860 when Wanostrocht & Co. built a stone breakwater pier. This is all that remains.

bolts in the sea wall are all that remain of the Kimmeridge Oil & Carbon Co.'s jetty of 1883. At Clavell's Hard to the east there are said to be traces cut into the tidal ledges for a 300-foot iron jetty designed by Evan Hopkins from 1858–60.

There were small shipping quays along the southern shore of the more sheltered waters of Poole Harbour. Ball clay was earlier shipped from the Arne peninsula but most was carried by tramways to be tipped down chutes into boats alongside quays at Middlebere, Ridge, and Goathorn in the nineteenth and early-twentieth centuries. Sailing barges took up to 30 tons from Middlebere, while 60-ton barges were towed from Ridge by a steam tug down to Poole for transshipment. Barges and steamships called at Goathorn until the 1930s. The timber pier at Middlebere is lost in the mud of a lonely creek, but some trace remains at Goathorn by the channel of South Deep. Not far from the site of the late-Iron Age port on the south side of Christchurch Harbour, Holloway's Dock (SZ 180908) served the iron ore quarries for a short period in the mid-nineteenth century. It was only suitable for barge traffic, and the channel cut through the salt marsh is still discernible today after years of abandonment and silting.

Goathorn Pier on Poole Harbour was once a shipping place for ball clay from pits at Newton and Norden.

The industrial archaeology of shipping includes lighthouses and other navigational lights, coastguard lookouts and houses. Portland Bill has three standing lighthouse towers, although only one is operational. The Bill and offshore tide race were notorious hazards, and Defoe noted 'they have, within these few months, set up two light-houses on the two points of that island.' These first Higher and Lower Lighthouses were built in 1716 with limited illumination provided by coal fires. John Smeaton 'did not fail' to visit them in May 1756, when he was searching Portland for stone for his own Eddystone Lighthouse. In 1788 the first Argand lamps to be fitted in an English lighthouse were installed in the Higher Light, in two rows of seven oil lamps with hollow wicks. Thomas Rogers also installed silvered glass reflectors and the first plano-convex lenses here. The Lower Lighthouse (SY 681690) was rebuilt in 1789 and a plaque commemorating the event is preserved inside the present lighthouse on the Bill. It reads:

*For
The Direction and Comfort
of NAVIGATORS;
For
The Benefit and Security of COMMERCE;
And For
A lasting Memorial
of BRITISH HOSPITALITY
To All Nations,
This Light-House was erected
By the ancient Corporation
of TRINITY-HOUSE
of Deptford-Strond
in 1789.
Distance from the Cliffs 608 Feet*

Both lighthouses were rebuilt in 1869, with new keepers' accommodation alongside in the typical Trinity House style of the period. Only a short tower was needed at the Higher Light because it stood at a higher elevation. Redundant since 1906, the Higher Light was converted to accommodation while the Lower Light became the Portland Bird Observatory in 1962. The present Portland Lighthouse *(SY 677684)* was built on the Bill in 1905–06. The tower is 136-feet (41.4m) high and its light is visible for 25 miles. Its keepers' accommodation became redundant when the lighthouse was automated in 1996 and now houses a visitor centre.

Portland Bill Lighthouse was built in 1905–06 to replace the old Higher and Lower Lights. The keepers' accommodation now contains a lighthouse visitor centre.

A prominent white obelisk at the very end of the Bill is inscribed 'TH 1844'. Trinity House erected this as a day-mark long before the present lighthouse, when this low tip of the island must have been difficult indeed to spot from seaward in poor visibility or rough weather. Offshore, a lightship marking the Shambles shoal is now replaced by a buoy. Portland's fourth lighthouse is an iron structure of 1908, erected at the end of the northeastern arm of the Breakwater.

Anvil Point Lighthouse *(SZ 029769)* was opened in 1881 after a series of tragic shipwrecks. It was

Portland Higher Light and keepers' accommodation.

The day-mark obelisk was erected by Trinity House in 1844 on the very tip of Portland Bill, long before the present light-house was built.

Portland Lower Light was rebuilt in 1869 and is now a bird observatory.

Anvil Point Lighthouse was built in 1881 to close a gap between the lighthouses at the Needles and Portland Bill.

provided with keepers' accommodation, the whole enclosed within a wall. The short tower is some 100 feet above sea level. It used oil until electrified in 1960 and a lens from this lighthouse is preserved in the Science Museum.

This discussion on shipping matters would be incomplete without a note on Portland Breakwater *(SY 697743* to *SY 683780)*, which is the largest artificial harbour in Britain and was the most massive civil engineering work undertaken in Dorset. It was built in two stages, the first from 1847–72 to the design of James Meadows Rendel, an engineer known in Devon for the Saltash and Torpoint ferries across the Tamar. John Leather was the main contractor. After Rendel died in 1856, the breakwater was completed by John Coode, who was knighted in 1872 at the completion of the great work. Coode also designed

repairs to West Bay Pier, a dam across the Backwater at Weymouth and an iron bridge at Ferrybridge.

Prince Albert laid the foundation stone on 25 July 1849 and Portland Breakwater was formally opened on 10 August 1872 by his son the Prince of Wales who visited on the Royal Yacht *Victoria & Albert*. Nearly 6 million tons of Portland stone went into the construction, quarried by convicts and carried by rail down the Breakwater Incline and across timber trestles for tipping into the sea. Blocks of up to 7 tons created a tipped mound or 'pierre perdue' 250-feet wide at its base 50 feet below low water. The arm from the Portland shore was separated from the main breakwater by the South Ship Channel. The top was finished in dressed stone, with the semi-circular ends faced in granite. Despite a huge fort

Portland Breakwater.

at the end of the breakwater, the development of advanced weaponry and the threat of torpedo attacks led to the complete enclosure of the anchorage by the North-Eastern Breakwater and Bincleaves Groyne from 1895–1905. Some 2 million tons of stone for this were brought from Portland in barges. The Victorian confidence and scale of this breakwater is in a league of its own compared to all other harbour works along the Dorset coast.

The iron lighthouse on the end of the northeastern arm of Portland Breakwater stands amid twentieth-century defensive works.

Coastguard lookout of 1804 at Charmouth. This humble building, at one time used by the Customs, is yet another aspect of the archaeology of ports, shipping and navigational aids.

21

✤ THE WATER SUPPLY INDUSTRY ✤

The Romans provided Dorset with its first engineered water supply when an aqueduct served the town of Durnovaria (Dorchester). This water leat contoured the west side of the Frome Valley for 5 miles to a presumed tank at the top end of Dorchester, from which the town's supply was distributed in lead pipes. Earthworks survive in Fordington Bottom and elsewhere, and recent excavations have demonstrated that the aqueduct was once covered and its source was a dam at Littlewood near Frampton. As with the roads, such a sophisticated system did not re-emerge until the Age of Steam. Within just a few miles of this rare Roman survival, Wessex Water maintains a museum at the Victorian water pumping station of Sutton Poyntz.

For centuries most villages and towns relied on wells or springs for their water supply, which in cases continued into the twentieth century. Handpumps or cast-iron fountains became common in the nineteenth century. The water supply industry was born in the mid-nineteenth century following the Public Health Act of 1848 which demanded good-quality piped water for the increasing populations in the towns in the wake of cholera and typhoid scares. Dorset's water requirements have always been extracted from springs, deep boreholes or rivers, without recourse to surface reservoirs. Ever since the Victorian period, filtered and treated water has been pumped up to holding reservoirs built at a high point from which customers are supplied by gravity. These may take the form of a covered tank or raised water tower.

Weymouth's water supply was greatly improved in 1856 when the Weymouth Waterworks Co. opened a new waterworks and pumping station, designed by the water engineer Thomas Hawksley, at Sutton Poyntz (SY 706839). Abundant springs in the Upper Greensand and Chalk were tapped at the Springhead, with a yield of up to 8 million gallons a day in winter. Here the overflow and filter incorporates part of

A typical small water fountain erected in 1859 for the benefit of villagers at Abbotsbury.

DERRICK WARREN

The preserved 1857 water turbine at Sutton Poyntz was in working order for a century.

a funnel from Brunel's *Great Eastern*, purchased by the water company when the ship put into Weymouth Bay after a mid-Channel explosion on her maiden voyage in 1859. The water was first pumped to a reservoir at Preston by two turbines made by David Cook & Co. of Glasgow in 1856–57. The surviving pump could pump 300,000 gallons per day (1.36 million litres) and was in working order until 1958 when electric pumps were installed. The pumping station was extended in 1869 to house a horizontal single-cylinder steam engine made by Joseph Whitham of Leeds, with pumps and boilers. There were further extensions in 1882 when two more Whitham engines were installed, and from 1899–1901 when a Gimson steam engine and two Lancashire boilers were added in new buildings. This was never reliable and was decommissioned in 1934 when a Hathorn Davey triple-expansion steam engine replaced the original 1869 engine. Twelve men were required to keep the two 1882 engines in steam until 1958 when electric pumps took over all work. Increasing demands for water in Weymouth necessitated the opening of a new source of water at a borehole site at Empool in 1934.

The buildings in Portland stone show the development stages at Sutton Poyntz, although

The Weymouth Water Co. built the Empool pumping station in the 1930s to develop a new water source. One of the two Brush, marine, flat four-diesel engines is seen here being assembled on site.

Development of steam pumping engine houses at Sutton Poyntz dating, right to left, from 1869, 1882 and 1899. The first building was heightened in 1934.

the chimney has gone. There is also a meter house of 1900, and the superintendent's house which is believed to have been the miller's house on the site before the waterworks was built. Although parts of the pumping station are still operational, Wessex Water opened a Museum of Water Supply here in 1989, adding displays of pumps, engines and other artefacts from elsewhere in the water industry.

In contrast to Sutton Poyntz, there is a much smaller site at Sherborne where pumps were worked by a waterwheel. Following outbreaks of cholera and typhoid, the people of Sherborne demonstrated it was possible to obtain water for their town that was reliable in both supply and quality. After abortive plans in 1852 to use turbines to pump water to a reservoir at Golden Ball, the Castleton Pumping Station *(ST 646169)* was

Water mains are the vital but hidden side of the water industry. This shows the washout assembly during the laying of the rising main from Empool pumping station to North Down reservoir, believed to be at West Knighton Farm, April 1937.

established at a borehole in 1869 with a waterwheel driving three vertical ram pumps supplied by Stothert & Pitt of Bath. This wheel was substantially rebuilt in 1898 by Edward White of Redditch. It is the largest wheel in Dorset, measuring 26-feet diameter by 3-feet 8-inches wide, and worked until 1959 when the pumps were scrapped. Water for the wheel was brought in at two levels from the Oborne Stream and Sherborne Park Lake. The small stone-built pumping station has been preserved by the Castleton Waterwheel Group. Nearby are stone buildings for later engines and pumps. A pump-house with a horizontal steam engine made by E.S. Hindley of Bourton was erected in 1876 to work alongside the waterwheel. In 1898 the pump-house was extended for a Crossley gas engine, and in 1928 and 1932 for two Petters' oil engines with Sulzer pump-sets. Electric pumping was installed in the war years.

The Castleton pump-house erected in 1876 for a steam engine and extended for other engines in 1898 and 1928–32.

Swanage has some interesting relics of the water industry, thanks largely to George Burt who was responsible for so many other curiosities in the town. He promoted the Swanage Water Works which was first built in 1864, and its old building in Sentry Road *(SZ 033786)* has details inscribed in stone. Water was pumped up the hill to a lead tank atop the prominent Durlston water tower *(SZ 032782)*, from where distribution to the town was by gravity. This was built in 1886 in stone with a corner turret, similar in style to Burt's 'Durlston Castle'. The tower is now part of a house.

George Burt was also involved in waterworks at Ulwell, where there were springs and a covered reservoir. The completion of this scheme was commemorated in 1892 by the erection of a tall granite obelisk on Ballard Down above *(SZ 022813)*. This monument had originally supported gas lamps in the City of London and was one of many items brought to the town in Burt's returning stone ships. The obelisk was pulled down in 1940 and re-erected in 1973. The Ulwell supply was unable to cope with the needs of Swanage and a new source was developed at a pumping station built in 1921 under the chalk escarpment beside the Studland road at Corfe Castle.

The Castleton Pumping Station at Sherborne, showing the corrugated iron housing for the giant waterwheel.

The upper leat (dry) from the Oborne stream approaching the Castleton water pumping station.

Water supplies at Dorchester were improved when the town corporation had a 300-foot shaft and borehole to the west of the town, from which a steam engine pumped water to a tower built in 1881 on higher ground. This water tower *(SY 684906)*, with an iron reservoir tank on brick-arched supports, dominates the skyline although it is now redundant.

Dorchester's water tower of 1881 has a circular iron tank supported by an octagonal pillared brick structure.

The stone water tower at Swanage was built in 1886. The height of the tank on top is recorded as 239 feet above sea level. Water was pumped up here from an artesian well at the Swanage Water Works in Sentry Road.

Water supply was difficult on the Isle of Portland, where the inhabitants relied on wells, springs and ponds. The Admiralty solved their own problem when Chene Pumping Station (SY 691702) was built in 1855 with a steam engine to pump water from springs to a reservoir near Folly Pier. The remains of the old pumping house stands on a cliff top at Freshwater Bay. Not far away an attempt was made at Southwell to find a good water supply for the people of Portland, when a well and bore were sunk in 1893 to a depth of 270 feet in the Portland Sand. Two side-headings were driven out but only one yielded water and this was found to be contaminated by sea water and decomposed sewage.

The first reliable piped water supply was instigated by the Portland Urban District Council who turned to Upwey north of Weymouth for a water supply. In 1897 a new shaft and borehole were sunk at Gould's Bottom (SY 660861) and a steam pumping station built for pumping water to a reservoir on Portland. The scheme first brought piped water to the island in 1900 although the reservoir was not completed for another two years. The stone reservoir, with an octagonal plan

and a small tower on one side, stands on the highest ground at Portland Heights (SY 689729). Yields at Gould's Bottom were not as great as expected and a new pumping station was built a short distance away at Friar Waddon in 1914. Two boreholes were sunk 360 feet into the chalk and initially yielded a reliable 900,000 gallons a day. Electric pumping was introduced in 1935. Pumping machinery remained at Gould's Bottom until about ten years before the works was demolished in 1970. The brick pumping station at Friar Waddon remains in the valley half a mile to the southwest (SY 652858).

Portland's octagonal stone reservoir was completed in 1902 on the hilltop at Portland Heights, and water was pumped here from near Upwey to the north of Weymouth.

The Bournemouth Gas & Water Co. of 1863 began taking water from a stream at Bourne Valley, which was then outside the town, but larger sources of water were required as demand rose. A steam pumping station was built in 1875 at Tuckton between the River Stour and Iford Lane *(SZ 146925)*, but this was a failure, mainly due to unstable sand in the well. The building had an interesting subsequent history, as Count Vladimir Tchertkov and fellow Russian émigrés took it over for their Free Age Press. Tolstoy's works were first printed here in 1900–13. The brick chimney remains, and the conversion of the works to housing won a Building Conservation Award in 1988. A water tower in Palmerston Road, Boscombe, was built in 1880 as part of this project *(SZ 112922)*. This large polychrome brick structure has been converted to accommodation.

A new site was opened in 1883 at Longham Mill *(SZ 064973)* on the River Stour where water was extracted from the valley gravels. A water turbine for pumping was found unreliable because of the river's irregular flow; steam plant was installed in 1888, and the Bourne Valley site was closed in the following year. There were more developments in the 1920s when extraction from the River Stour now required water filtration plant. An Armfield turbine was tried briefly from 1920–24. A new river extraction source was opened in 1949 at Matchams on the River Avon and took over from Longham.

The search for new water supplies was not over because Bournemouth continued to grow rapidly. The water company developed a new source from the underground chalk aquifer at Wimborne where they established a handsome pumping station at Walford Bridge *(SU 007009)* from 1896–1904. The pumps were worked by Simpson compound tandem steam engines which ran until electric pumps took over in 1959. Treatment plant was installed to soften the water and remove mineral deposits. The station had a complex of wells and headings. The main pumping well was 256-feet deep, through river gravel and Reading beds into the upper chalk. It was 10-feet diameter down to 210 feet, lined with cast-iron to 170 feet. A 6-inch bore continued to the bottom. Headings (collecting tunnels) were driven at depths of 155 feet and 195 feet. One effect of this scheme was to reduce the hydrostatic pressure of water from the chalk, which was felt at Wimborne and Kingston Lacy. Before, the pressure had been such that a 3-inch bore made at Ellis's brewery in 1867 flooded the yard by a spout of water 'of considerable height'.

Bournemouth obtained a new water supply in 1904 from a 256-foot borehole in the chalk aquifer at Walford Bridge, Wimborne. Steam engines worked here until 1959.

The impressive Parkstone water tower dates from 1883.

Water was pumped from Longham and Wimborne to the Alderney Works *(SZ 046950)* which was established in the 1880s and became the main centre for water treatment and storage. This site was expanded from 1893–1902 and again in the 1920s and 1930s when a large covered reservoir was built.

Poole inhabitants gained an early water supply in 1542, when they were allowed to build a conduit from near Canford Magna to the town. The Poole Waterworks Co. was established by an Act in 1859 and water was first drawn from springs at Constitution Hill and later at Hatch Pond. After the Poole Corporation took over in

1906, a new well and pumping station was built at Corfe Mullen *(SY 971984)*. The Admiralty also opened a water pumping station at Corfe Mullen for the Holton Heath cordite factory in 1914. This was taken into the domestic supply network in 1966. A new source for Poole was developed at Sturminster Marshall in the 1950s. Two large water towers were built, each with a capacity of 60,000 gallons, at Parkstone *(SZ 042921)* in 1883 and at Broadstone *(SZ 012958)* in 1894.

Another water tower, in striking orange brick and with corner pinnacles, stands at Seafield Gardens in Southbourne *(SZ 142915)*. Now redundant, it was built in 1897 by the West Hampshire Water Co. This company increased pumping power at the site of Knapp Mill *(SZ 155938)* on the River Avon in the 1920s in response to developments around Christchurch and the eastern suburbs of Bournemouth. Two pumping houses were built in 1928 and 1937, the latter with the appearance of a chapel. Today, the Bournemouth and West Hampshire companies have amalgamated.

The brick water tower at Seafield Gardens, Southbourne, was built by the West Hampshire Water Co. in 1897.

Not a chapel, but the pumping house built in 1937 by the West Hampshire Waterworks at the Knapp Mill site near Christchurch.

22

☙ LIGHT, HEAT AND POWER ☙

The dirty Victorian gasworks was never a place of charm, yet played an essential part in many towns for more than a century until the introduction of natural gas. From the 1830s coal or town gas was first supplied for street lighting, but within thirty years or so its use for domestic lights, cookers and heaters became more widespread as the gas companies expanded their industry. By-products which could be sold were coke, tar, ammonia and fertilisers.

Bituminous coal was heated in horizontal retorts placed in rows in the retort house, leaving coke. The exhauster drew gas from the retorts to pass it through the condenser for cooling and separating the tar, the scrubber to remove ammonia in water, and the purifiers which used lime or iron oxide. A steam engine drove the exhauster and pump for the scrubber. Later retorts were vertical, which could be used continuously. The purified gas was stored in the gasholder which was sealed with water at the base. Early gasholders were held between columns but spiral guided types were invented in 1890. Gas was supplied to consumers by a network of pipes laid by the company.

Dorset's first gasworks was opened in 1832 at Bridport and within a few years there were undertakings at Beaminster, Dorchester, Gillingham, Lyme Regis, Poole, Portland, Shaftesbury, Sherborne, Stalbridge, Sturminster Newton, Swanage, Weymouth and Wimborne, while Bournemouth and Christchurch (in Hampshire) also had gasworks. Private estates had small gasworks for their own consumption, such as at Motcombe House in north Dorset in the 1880s. Each supplied its locality and was completely isolated. Some companies had already integrated when the gas industry was nationalised in 1949. A grid main was laid to supply the outlying towns with gas from the larger works, such as Poole, and the small uneconomical gasworks were closed during the 1950s. The discovery of North Sea natural gas in 1964 had a far greater impact on the industry, which resulted in the closure of all traditional gasworks.

The gasworks never had a good public image and demolition and redevelopment were no doubt welcomed with some relief. Nevertheless, some evidence does survive from this once important industry, including retort buildings, offices and houses. The best of these are at Bridport, Dorchester and Swanage.

The Bridport Gas Co. was the first in Dorset when it was established in 1831 and the Bridport gasworks (SY 465923) was opened in the following year in South Street. The cast-iron horizontal retorts were purchased from the Neath Abbey Iron Co., shipped around from South Wales to Bridport Harbour. Coal for manufacturing gas was also imported by sea before the railway came to the town. The gasworks survived nationalisation for a few years, but after closure in 1958 most of the site was cleared. Today, houses have been developed here, but the former entrance on South Street is still flanked by two gasworks buildings in local stone. On one side is the manager's house with a stone inscribed 'BGC 1872', while nearest the town centre is the showroom building of 1899.

Staff outside the Bridport Gas Co.'s new showroom building in about 1900. The gasworks site, seen in background, has been developed for housing.

BRIDPORT MUSEUM

Another early gasworks was established by Benjamin Porter in late-1832 at Beaminster in an old tan yard in Shadrack Street. The Beaminster Gas, Coal & Coke Co. was soon formed to supply gas for lighting but after losing money the company sold the works in 1849 to the Beaminster Gas Association. The gasworks moved to an old quarry at Clampits at the end of St Mary Well Street in 1860, where a gasholder was supplied by John Smith of Chard. The Beaminster Gas Co. Ltd, registered in 1868, built a second gasholder in 1869, this time supplied by Edward Cockey of Frome. The Gas House, rebuilt in 1896, recalls the industry here (ST 479001). In 1927 a new large gasholder replaced the two old ones and ten years later the works had been acquired by the Crewkerne Gas & Coke Co. Ltd when there were still 41 street lights in the town lit by gas.

The Sherborne Gas & Coke Co. opened a gasworks in 1836 and it grew to have 52 retorts producing 363,000 cubic feet a day until closure in 1957. It was conveniently placed for receiving coal via the railway, from which a siding with a turntable ran into the works. The railway opened in 1860 and may account for a new building at the gasworks in 1864. Much of the site was sold off and cleared four years after closure, but some buildings such as the manager's house stand in Gashouse Hill, just south of the railway station *(ST 641161)*. In the town, Sherborne Museum displays a small No.5 Alcazar steam engine manufactured by E.S. Hindley & Sons in 1925 for driving tar and liquid pumps at the gasworks.

The Shaftesbury Gas & Coke Co. Ltd was established in 1836 with a gasworks on a site at Bimport *(ST 859229)* and Gillingham's gas company followed in 1837. Coal was brought from the Radstock area of the Somerset coalfield. In 1928 the companies were amalgamated to form the Shaftesbury, Gillingham & District Gas Co. Ltd. Both the small works ceased in the 1950s after nationalisation and were subsequently cleared. The site of the Shaftesbury gasworks is now occupied by the ambulance station.

Weymouth's gasworks in Westway Road was established in 1836 and run by its builder W.W. Burdon until 1867 when it was taken over by the new Weymouth Gas Consumers Co. Ltd. The gasworks was enlarged in 1933 on land reclaimed from the Backwater. Long-since closed, the site retains a large gasholder which dominates the Backwater. For many years a stone structure standing in the Backwater contained a shaft giving access to a tunnel bearing the gas main into the town.

On Portland, a gasworks was built in the early-1860s in Victoria Square, Chiswell, where it was convenient for obtaining coal from the railway terminus. It was built privately for William Burden, but it was never a success and was often flooded by the sea. After 1876, Richard Howard owned the works, but sold out to Portland Council at the turn of the century. The new convict prison on Portland had its own gasworks by 1850.

The first gasworks at Swanage was opened in 1867 and the town was soon well lit, relieving a want that 'had long been considered a drawback' according to a local guidebook. It was rebuilt in 1882 some distance from the town centre *(SZ 020792)*, perhaps anticipating the arrival of the Swanage Railway three years later when it was given its own siding. It closed in about 1925, but the solid-stone retort house in Victoria Avenue has found another industrial use as a workshop for the Greystone Garage. Next to the road, in the Triangle Service Station's forecourt, a small weighing house bears the stone inscription: 'SWANAGE GAS WORKS

The stone retort house of the Swanage gasworks, seen from the north.

BUILT 1867, REBUILT 1882. Established 16 and 17 Victoria ch 16'. The petrol tanks are said to be sunk in the hole of the gasholder.

The Dorchester Gas & Coke Co. began in 1835 and the site of the gas works *(SY 905659)* in Icen Way retains a number of buildings, now occupied by Wood's removal stores. Of particular interest is a curving roadway into the site with stone setts and two lines of granite slabs, designed to bear the heavy wheels of coal and coke wagons, and still in fine condition long after closure of the gasworks.

Although most of Weymouth's gasworks site has been cleared, the telescopic gasholder still dominates the Backwater.

Granite setts were laid down for heavy coal and coke wagons entering and leaving the Dorchester gasworks site off Icen Way.

it opened in December 1925 it was the most modern in the country. Its 136 vertical retorts produced 14 million cubic feet of gas per day using coal shipped from northeast England and delivered from the quay by aerial ropeway. During the Second World War a large hydrogen plant was built here for making gas for barrage balloons. When the gas industry was nationalised in 1949, gas was being supplied to a wide area, including Blandford, Wareham, Fordingbridge and Lymington. Poole gasworks was the last to close. Three gasholders survive at the Bourne Valley site *(SZ 060926)*.

Gasholders at Bourne Valley, the site of the first gasworks of the Bournemouth Gas & Water Co. in 1863.

It is of particular surprise and interest that gas street lighting, one of its earliest uses, is still functioning in the conservation area of Holdenhurst near Bournemouth. This is remarkable in the early-twenty-first century when we have grown so accustomed to electric lights dominating our townscapes at night. From the late-nineteenth century electricity began to rival gas, first for lighting and then for power and heating. In 1900 waterwheels, turbines or stationary engines drove small generators for very local consumption, but within sixty years a large electric power station at Poole supplied the county through a grid and there were even experimental nuclear plants at Winfrith. Electricity had now become the vital source for domestic lighting and heating, street lighting and the power for running most industrial machinery. For consumers, electricity was a cleaner, safer and more convenient alternative to gas although it cannot be stored. The distribution of mains electricity by wires and poles enabled the remotest farms to be accessed, where a piped gas supply would have been out of the question. On a larger scale, a national grid system was well established by the 1930s, and pylon towers and sub-station sites of this era are old enough to be considered part of the industrial archaeology of the county.

Poole and Bournemouth were served by their own gas companies until about 1900. The first gasworks had been established in 1833 at the east end of Poole Quay by the Poole Gas & Coke Co. The Bournemouth Gas & Water Co. built a gasworks in 1863 at Bourne Valley, then 2 miles outside the growing town, and all coal landed at Poole Quay had to be brought in by horse wagons. At the turn of the century the company bought the better-placed Poole gasworks and vertical retorts were developed here by the assistant engineer Arthur Duckham. The Christchurch gasworks was also taken over but the foundry and repair shops remained at Bourne Valley. A new large Poole gasworks was begun in 1924 on reclaimed land at Pitwines and when

Electricity pylons crossing the ridgeway to the north of Corton. Transmission lines are now becoming part of industrial archaeology.

had four steam engines, built in 1895 and 1904, for electricity generation and supplying hot water and heating in 1950. The hospital was an early user of carbon filament lamps.

In towns, the first supplies were often private affairs connected with a few neighbours, such as the dynamo set which supplied the first domestic electricity in Blandford Forum, now restored and displayed in the town's museum. Bridport's own Municipal Electric Power Station *(SY 463933)* at St Swithin's Road, Allington, was built by George Abbot & Son in 1929. Two Ruston & Hornsby oil engines ran two Harland alternators with a generating capacity of 286 kilowatts. Three years later electricity was being supplied as far as Beaminster. After becoming redundant, this striking building in brick with a clerestory roof has become the church bell works of Nicholson Engineering Ltd. Other towns had less substantial power stations. The Sherborne Electricity Co.'s works was built in 1923 and had three petrol and oil engines to drive the generators. A power station was built at Castletown in 1906 for the purposes of the naval base, but the domestic population of Portland had to wait until 1930 when mains electricity was first supplied from Weymouth.

Bridport's electricity power station was opened in 1929.

Mains electricity became more widely available in rural areas when the industry was nationalised after the Second World War. Until then small generator sets were used in larger houses, some institutions and factories, either driven by water, gas, steam or petrol. Many watermills powered small generators for their own consumption or for private estates. The waterwheel at Trigon Farm ran a generator in 1901, and a waterwheel at Folly Mill, Bridport, was being used for electricity generation as late as 1950. Mr Newman of Taunton installed electric lighting in Fordington steam mill, Dorchester, in 1892. After it was burnt down in 1894, Canford Mill, near Wimborne, was converted to generate electricity using three 45-inch diameter 'British Empire' Armfield turbines. The isolated Herrison Hospital near Charminster still

Poole Power Station with its two 325-foot chimneys became a major Dorset landmark at Hamworthy after it was built from 1949–52. It had been planned by the Bournemouth & Poole Electricity Supply Co. Ltd, before being overtaken by nationalisation under the Central Electricity Generating Board. Generation began in December 1950 and the last of four turbo-alternators was commissioned in 1952. The station was designed to burn pulverised coal, but in 1954 it was converted to oil-burning and extended by installing two more generator sets. This brought the output to 340,000 kilowatts, which was large for Dorset at the time, but small in comparison with modern power stations. The station was conveniently sited on the shore of Holes Bay, where coasters negotiated Poole Bridge to bring the coal, and then the oil. Electricity was generated at 11,800 volts, and stepped up to 132,000 volts by transformers to be fed into the national grid. Sea water was drawn from Holes Bay for condensing the steam which drove the turbines, turning it back into pure water for reuse in the boilers. After generation ceased, this great building was demolished in 1993–94.

Dorset is fortunate to have the Museum of Electricity in the engine and boiler houses of a former power station at Bargates, Christchurch *(SZ 156931)*. The power station was opened by the Bournemouth & Poole Electricity Supply Co. in 1903, when Christchurch was in Hampshire, and it may be the only substantial Edwardian power station left standing in Britain. As well as serving the residents and street lighting in the town, electricity was also supplied to the trams that ran to Bournemouth and Poole. Generation ceased in 1926 when a national grid was being established and the buildings housed a sub-station and store. Much of this has been moved

outside to give space for the museum. Original features inside include the cast-iron staircase and landing from which the control engineer could supervise the generating hall, and ornate support pillars for the station's overhead crane. Exhibits include a Bellis & Morcom/GEC generating set similar to the two steam engines installed in the station in 1903, and a generator and Armfield turbine of 1925 from Ringwood's hydro-electric station.

The many exhibits illustrate the history of the electricity supply industry over a century, and this is the place to study early laboratory equipment, generators, switchgear, transformers, appliances, lighting and wiring systems. There is even a statue of Phoebe, Goddess of the Moon, that was made for the 1882 electricity exhibition at Crystal Palace. Pride of place is the electric Bournemouth Tram Car No.85, the only complete example of its type. It ran on the system from 1914 until closure in 1936, and then worked at Llandudno until 1954. It was purchased by the Science Museum and restored by Bournemouth Corporation staff.

The Edwardian power station at Bargates, Christchurch, now houses the Museum of Electricity.

Street junction box at the Museum of Electricity.

23

❧ HOUSING AND RECREATION ❧

There were occasions when accommodation was purpose-built for industrial workers and a study of this type of housing is long overdue. Examples in towns include small terraces associated with breweries at Wyke, Gillingham, and the Old Brewery, Bridport, or the gas company's terrace of ten cottages along Bimport in Shaftesbury. Richard Roberts' terrace of 1800 at Burton Bradstock for flax workers, and the housing at Pymore village have been described in chapter 14. Many houses were built in connection with the Westbury silk mill at Sherborne, where Robert Willmott built a striking terrace at Horsecastles in the 1850s, followed by eight 'respectable houses' in South Street. Later, Rev. Joseph Ogle and Samuel le Mare of the silk mill formed the Sherborne Cottage Building Co. and built at least 90 cottages, all 'models of neatness and comfort'. The company remained separate from the silk mill when the latter was sold in 1907.

These cottages near the Old Brewery at Bridport were built for the workers.

Cottages built at Bimport by the Shaftesbury Gasworks Company.

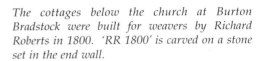

The cottages below the church at Burton Bradstock were built for weavers by Richard Roberts in 1800. 'RR 1800' is carved on a stone set in the end wall.

Terraced housing at the industrial village of Pymore near Bridport.

An impressive terrace of workers' houses at Horsecastles, Sherborne, built by Robert Willmott in the 1850s.

Houses were built for employees or as speculations close to a number of brickworks. One of the most impressive is at Sandford, near Wareham, where Sandford Terrace is in local pale brick *(SY 929895)*. New houses were erected for workers after the Whitehead Torpedo Factory was opened in 1891 at Wyke Regis. These included Ferrybridge Cottages and others along Portland Road, and the firm even provided a school for the community in Victoria Road in 1897.

Housing was essential at remote industrial sites, such as on Branksea (Brownsea) Island where there were high hopes of a large clay and pottery industry in 1855. Colonel Waugh built a new set-

tlement on the northwest side of the island, naming it Maryland after his wife. Here in 1881, the Census recorded the Island Inn and store (G. Petts, wife and two servants) and 107 other inhabitants. An infants' school was held in one of the houses. This model village *(SZ 023883)* of 19 houses arranged in five blocks was damaged in the Second World War and was demolished in 1963. Newton *(SZ 013847)* was a settlement created at the Newton Heath clay pits in the 1860s and this too was damaged in the war. At Kimmeridge, the shale enterprise of Wanostrocht & Co. was short-lived but their terrace of workers' cottages built from 1858–60 at Gaulter Gap is still occupied *(SY 908792)*.

More exposed accommodation was provided for lighthouse keepers and their families. Exposure came with the lighthouse's location, and in 1855 Walter White described the keeper's garden at Portland's Higher Lighthouse with flowers and 'a plantation of shrubs and small trees under the seaward wall, but all shorn off even with the wall top by the mere force of the wind.' Anvil Point Lighthouse had a wall surrounding a very exposed garden of about an acre where, in 1882, Robinson considered 'it will be a wonder if anything ever grows there above the degree of a cabbage'. Coastguard houses at St Aldhelm's Head, for example, are equally exposed. Those on the sheltered east side of Brownsea Island were built in 1842 more stylishly with crenellations.

On the land, farm and estate workers were provided with better housing by the more enlightened landlords. In 1854, Louis Ruegg discussed improved cottages built by the principal landowners. Sturt set the example, with cottages on his scattered properties 'easily recognised by their comfortable and uniform appearance', followed by Lord Portman (at Durweston and Pimperne), the Earl of Ilchester (Abbotsbury and Evershot), Duke of Bedford (Swyre entirely rebuilt), Lord Shaftesbury, Sir R.P. Glyne and Mr Williams of Bridehead. A dormitory for ten single men was in use from about 1853 at Bryanston Farm (see page 20), where 'the arrangements promise to conduce to the comfort of the men and the good of the farm.'

A whole range of other specialist buildings or structures serving spiritual or secular pleasures can be found within the period of the Age of Steam. This wide-ranging subject includes Nonconformist chapels, coaching inns, schools, halls and institutes, pleasure parks, bandstands, ornamental clocks (as in Weymouth and Dorchester), early cinemas (the gas-lit Rex at Wareham is a notable example) and tearooms. In contrast there are hospitals, workhouses (alas, many), lock-ups and prisons (notably Portland and Dorchester).

Anvil Point and its lighthouse keepers' accommodation, enclosed by a wall where C.E. Robinson felt nothing greater than a cabbage would grow.

Primitive Methodist Chapel of 1854 at King's Stag in the Blackmoor Vale. Nonconformist chapels served the working classes in the towns and countryside.

Coastguard houses of about 1842 near the landing stage on Brownsea Island, not of the typical windswept type but nevertheless an interesting group.

A former chapel built from corrugated iron at the junction of Marston and Coombe Road, Sherborne. Buildings of such a useful material were common in the later-nineteenth century.

These last two are a world apart from the delights of the fledgling tourist industry that developed from the late-eighteenth and throughout the nineteenth centuries. The popularisation by George III and other members of royalty of sea bathing and holidaying at the coastal resort of Weymouth is well known. The grateful inhabitants even erected a fine monument to their king on the esplanade, described in 1830 as 'one of the most charming promenades in England.' Nottington aspired to be a spa, but it was to be another twenty-seven years before Weymouth saw the arrival of the mainline railway and the first real opportunity to exploit a wider tourist market. Railways influenced seaside tourism to a lesser extent at Swanage and Bridport. The latter was less successful, despite changing its name to West Bay with the arrival of the branch extension here in 1884. Plans to promote a resort got as far as building Pier Terrace in 1885 near the harbour and an Esplanade in 1887. Bournemouth remained aloof in its early years of development, but after railway access improved in the 1880s it grew into the main coastal resort, with piers and cliff railways as part of the scene.

Seaside pleasures: Bournemouth developed into a major resort, complete with pier (rebuilt) and cliff railways.

24

❧ MATTERS OF DEFENCE ❧

The archaeology of war in Dorset's Age of Steam includes an outstanding concentration of coastal defences around Portland Harbour. Here, massive Victorian forts carried on a tradition of protecting the anchorage begun 400 years earlier with Henry VIII's gun forts at Portland and Sandsfoot. A perceived threat from the French, combined with improvements in firepower and accuracy in the late-1850s, led to a Royal Commission advising on the defences of British dockyards in 1860. The Verne was already under construction but the Commission recommended the Nothe Fort at Weymouth, and another on the end of the new Portland Breakwater. Although never used in anger, these expensive 'Palmerston Follies' proved a suitable deterrent in their day.

The Verne Citadel was begun on the highest summit of Portland during the construction work on the new breakwater works in the late-1840s, and a ditch at least 60-feet deep encircled a great rampart containing bomb-proof barracks. The ditch also provided thousands of tons of stone for the breakwater and a railway connected with the top of the Breakwater Incline. Huge rifled muzzle-loading guns (RMLs) were installed here. Outside the Verne there is little to see save the massive grassy rampart above the great ditch, rock-cut and partly reinforced with masonry. The monumental North Gate high above the harbour provides the main entrance through a long tunnel into the fort. The South Gate was completed in 1881 with a canopier for defensive fire and a drawbridge across the ditch. Below the citadel, the East Weares barracks, magazines and gun batteries were built in the same period, with

The great ditch around the Verne Citadel, seen at the South Gate.

yet another battery on the Inner Pier of the breakwater. All were manned by men of the Royal Artillery and served, with modifications, until the end of the Second World War; the Verne became a prison after 1948.

The Portland Breakwater Fort with its granite and armour-plated casemates never fails to impress.

The circular Breakwater Fort was built as an independent structure at the end of the breakwater with a base of concrete and dressed granite supporting thick armour plated casemates. Fourteen 12½-inch RML guns were planned, although not all were installed in 1874–75. There were barracks for 150 men and the fort was serviced through its own small harbour. Steam power was brought in to handle ammunition after 1884. This futurist fort still impresses. The Nothe Fort at Weymouth was built from 1860–72 to work with the Breakwater Fort. Weymouth Civic Society has skilfully restored this fort.

A later development on Portland from 1888–92 was the High Angle Battery (*SY 694732*), built in concrete with six gun emplacements and underground magazines. The six 9-inch RML guns were fitted to carriages enabling them to fire as howitzers with a range of 10,500 yards. A small tramway brought the shells to an upper level where they could be loaded into the muzzles of the guns. This battery, completely hidden from the sea, fired at a high angle and the 'plunging fire' dropped shells onto the more vulnerable decks of unsuspecting warships. The battery ceased in 1907

The High Angle Battery, Portland, was built in 1892 with concrete emplacements for six 9-inch RML guns. It became obsolete in 1907 although the magazines continued to be used.

and the guns were removed three years later. Meanwhile, Blacknor Fort *(SY 680716)* was completed high on the west coast in January 1902. The magazines of the High Angle Battery were used in both world wars.

On the land, tanks were a new development in the First World War and Bovington was chosen as a training centre in 1916. A 2-mile railway branch from Wool worked from 1919–28; thereafter tanks were loaded or unloaded at sidings at Wool. The embankment and a bridge abutment at the River Frome can be seen just north of Wool Station. There was much activity at Blandford Camp to which a railway branch operated from 1918–21.

Two factories were opened in Dorset to supply the Royal Navy with weaponry. The Whitehead Torpedo Factory *(SY 667763)* was established by Robert Whitehead on the shore of Portland Harbour near Ferrybridge at Wyke Regis in 1891. It became a major source of employment, with new houses built for workers and a new halt opened on the Weymouth & Portland Railway.

After closure it became a factory occupied by Wellworthy Engineering but the last part was demolished in 1997.

The Royal Naval Cordite Factory at Holton Heath *(SY 950910)* was Dorset's largest industrial site which employed thousands. It was established on the orders of Winston Churchill, then First Lord of the Admiralty, who insisted on a supply of cordite propellant for shells of the very highest quality. Holton Heath was well chosen, as it was a level barren site with access to a railway and the sea, and it was remote yet near a large pool of labour. The factory opened in January 1916, with some workers being transferred here from the Royal Gunpowder Factory at Waltham Abbey. Water was brought from a steam pumping station at Corfe Mullen to a reservoir on Black Hill within the site. The factory was spread over hundreds of acres and included a nitroglycerine plant, gun-cotton factory, a boiler house, electricity generating station, gasworks, laboratories, workshops, messes and canteen. There were 5 miles of sidings from the LSWR and an extension to a jetty at Rocklea from which sailing barges took cordite to Gosport and Chatham. In addition there were 14 miles of narrow-gauge line within the factory. The railways were worked by fireless locomotives, using high-pressure steam. There were battery locomotives too.

This shed served the locomotives working the 14 miles of narrow-gauge railway on the site of the Holton Heath cordite factory.

Acetone was vital in the incorporation of nitro-glycerine and gun-cotton. The biochemist Dr Chaim Weizmann, later the first President of Israel, developed a large acetone factory at Holton Heath. This was a fermentation process using maize, and later artichokes; horse chestnuts and acorns were used too. Eight large concrete fermentation vessels were built and 20,000 tons were produced during the war. In 1927 a new solvent-less cordite was developed and the acetone factory became redundant. The fermentation vessels were never demolished and became air-raid shelters in the Second World War. They remain today.

Acetone fermentation tanks at the Holton Heath cordite factory. Chaim Weizmann developed the process here during the First World War and the eight large concrete vessels were used as air-raid shelters in the next war.

sites at Arne and Wareham to divert enemy bombers. After the war, all explosives production was transferred to a new factory at Caerwent in Wales, but picrite was made at Holton Heath from 1950–56 and rocket propellant from 1952–57. The factory closed in 1957 but the Admiralty Materials Laboratories, established ten years before, remained. Today, a large acreage has become a nature reserve; there is an industrial estate and some remnants of the original factory are still standing.

A serious explosion occurred on 23 June 1931 when about 1½ tons of nitroglycerine blew up, killing ten workers and injuring 19 others. During the Second World War a picrite factory made flashless cordite. There were many air-raid warnings, but damage was successfully minimised by the application of two decoy

Recent years have seen a new interest in the archaeology of the Second World War, particularly as Dorset played a significant role in the D-day operations. Two 'Mulberry' harbour units at Castletown are a physical reminder of this. Coastal searchlights, gun emplacements and observation towers were used in both world wars, but other features were unique to the second conflict.

The extruded cordite testing building at the Holton Heath cordite factory. This building has a Belfast truss roof.

Surviving Second World War coastal defences include concrete anti-tank cubes or dragons' teeth, although they have been cleared at places like Charmouth. Good examples remain at Pondfield, Worbarrow Bay *(SY 871797)* and Kimmeridge. Pillboxes guarded all possible landing points. These range from a standard example overlooking the small opening from the beach at Eype Mouth *(SY 448910)*, to a circular Type 25 pillbox at Gaulter Gap, Kimmeridge *(SY 908791)*. The latter was made with corrugated iron shuttering and now leans over due to erosion of the beach. The valley mouth at Seacombe has an Allen Williams turret pillbox with a rotating domed steel roof *(SY 985767)*. Unusual conversions to pillboxes include the ground floor of the south windmill on Portland and a limekiln commanding the Fleet and Chesil Beach, while another limekiln at Yetminster was modified as an observation post *(ST 600103)*. Inland, there are examples of anti-tank cubes at Blandford Forum, while there is a small pillbox on the Sturminster Marshall side of White Mill Bridge.

This circular Type 25 pillbox at Gaulter Gap, Kimmeridge, is less common than the more usual Second World War designs.

A double line of anti-tank cubes makes an effective defence of a potential landing place at Pondfield, Worbarrow.

Heavy anti-aircraft batteries (one survives on Portland) and radar stations were new in the Second World War. For a while Worth Matravers was the centre of radar experiments of national importance before the unit was moved away north to a safer location. A tank range had been established at Lulworth before the war, but new ranges were opened at Tyneham, where the whole village was evacuated. There were ranges too at Studland, where the beaches were used as training for landings. A concrete observation bunker (Fort Henry) has been preserved overlooking the beaches. There were decoy sites at Arne, Goathorn and Brownsea Island to lure bombers away from Poole and the Holton Heath cordite factory.

Four Second World War airfields have left surprisingly little of their runways, dispersals, hangars, control towers or other buildings. Warmwell (*SY 760885*) was opened as Woodsford in 1937 for training and became a fighter base in 1941. After closure in 1945 it was a food depot and gravel has been quarried here since 1973. The control tower has been converted to a house. Tarrant Rushton (*ST 946058*) was developed in 1942–43 and was used for SOE operations and the airborne invasions of Normandy and Arnhem. It was a V-bomber standby airfield in the 1950s and Flight Refuelling Ltd was here from 1948 until moving to Hurn when the airfield closed in 1980.

Two T2-type hangars remain among the fields on this large airfield site overlooked by the earlier defensive earthworks of Badbury Rings.

Christchurch (*SZ 185932*) was a private airfield requisitioned in 1940, becoming the site of a shadow factory for Airspeed Ltd. This was taken over by De Havilland in 1951 and aircraft production ceased in 1962. Industrial estates and housing now cover the site, but famous aircraft live on in the street names. Hurn (*SZ 115980*) was opened in 1941. BOAC, which used Poole Harbour as a flying boat terminal, was at Hurn for two years from November 1944 before transferring to London Airport. In the 1950s Vickers-Armstrong Ltd manufactured the Viscount aeroplane here. Hurn subsequently developed into the Bournemouth International Airport.

Of equal importance were the ancillary buildings and structures of brick and concrete and the well-known Nissen huts, found on a wide range of sites. All twentieth-century military works, of whatever type, have left some trace in the landscape. Whether foundations or anchor points for radio masts, they all have a story to tell. They are as relevant to Dorset's history as medieval castles and they bring archaeology forcefully into the twentieth century. They stand alongside the more familiar industrial archaeology of Dorset's Age of Steam.

❧ SELECTED FURTHER READING ❧

General

J.H. Bettey, *The Island and Royal Manor of Portland* (Portland, 1970)

J. Claridge, *General View of the Agriculture in the County of Dorset* (1793)

J. Coker, *A Survey of Dorsetshire* (1793: actually by T. Gerrard, c.1625)

A.J. Cooksey, 'The Wren & Hopkinson horizontal cross compound engine, c.1870', *Industrial Archaeology*, 7 (1970), 165–70

A.J. Cooksey, *The Development of Communications in the Dorset area* (Dorchester, 1974)

P.W. Cox & C.M. Hearne, *Redeemed from the Heath: The Archaeology of the Wytch Farm Oilfield* (Dorchester, 1991)

D. Defoe, *A Tour Through the Whole Island of Great Britain* (1724–26)

M. Eedle, *A History of Beaminster* (Chichester, 1984)

J.P. Ferris, 'Alum at Kimmeridge', *SDNQ*, XXIX (1969), 81–85

D. Lewer & J.B. Calkin, *Curiosities of Swanage or Old London by the Sea* (Dorchester, 1971)

S. Morris, *Portland: An Illustrated History* (Wimborne, 1985)

N. Sunter & P.J. Woodward, *Romano-British Industries in Purbeck* (Dorchester, 1987)

D. Crossley, 'Sir William Clavell's Glasshouse at Kimmeridge, Dorset: The Excavations of 1980–81', *Archaeological Journal*, 144 (1987), 340–382

K. Falconer, *Guide to England's Industrial Heritage* (1980)

K. Hudson, *Industrial Archaeology of Southern England* (Newton Abbot, 1965; 2nd ed., 1968)

J. Hutchins, *The History and Antiquities of Dorset* (1774; 3rd ed. in 4 vols, 1861–70)

B. Kerr, *Bound to the Soil: A Social History of Dorset 1750–1918* (1968)

R. Legg, *Purbeck Island* (Milborne Port, 1972)

R. Legg, *Brownsea: Dorset's Fantasy Island* (Milborne Port, 1986)

R. Legg, *Purbeck's Heath, claypits, nature and the oilfield* (Milborne Port, 1987)

R. Lord, 'Industrious Gillingham, parts 1–3' *Dorset County Magazine*, 30–32 (1973)

R.A. Otter (ed.), *Civil Engineering Heritage: Southern England* (1994)

W. Page (ed.), *Victoria County History of Dorset* (1908)

R.J. Saville, *The Industrial Archaeology and Transport of Purbeck* (Basingstoke, 1976)

P. Stanier, *Dorset's Industrial Heritage* (Truro, 1989)

P. Stanier, *Discover Dorset: The Industrial Past* (Wimborne, 1998)

W. Stevenson, *General View of the Agriculture of the County of Dorset* (1815)

M.B. Weinstock, *Old Dorset* (Newton Abbot, 1967)

Farming in the Industrial Age

J.H. Bettey, *Man and the Land: 150 years of Dorset Farming 1846–1946* (Dorchester, 1996)

J.H. Bettey, *Discover Dorset: Farming* (Wimborne, 2000)

G. Boswell, *A Treatise on Watering Meadows* (1779)

H.S.L. Dewar, 'Flax, hemp and their growers in West Dorset', *PDNHAS*, 91 (1969), 216–9

W. Marshall, *The Rural Economy of the West of England* (2 vols, 1796)

A. Penny, 'Icehouses in Dorset', *PDNHAS*, 86 (1964), 203–230

M.S. Ross, 'Water meadows on the River Stirchel, Dorset', *PDNHAS*, 116 (1994), 27–32

L.H. Ruegg, 'Farming of Dorsetshire', *Jnl Royal Agric. Soc. of England*, 15, pt II, No. XXIV (1854), 389–454

B.J. Whitehead, 'The management and land-use of water meadows in the Frome Valley, Dorset', *PDNHAS*, 89 (1967), 257–281

R. Whitlock, *Dorset Farming* (Wimborne, 1982)

Dorset Stone

E. Benfield, *Purbeck Shop: a Stoneworker's Story of Stone* (1940; new edition, Southampton, 1990)

N. Bezzant, *Out of the Rock...*, (1980)

T. Haysom, 'Extracting Purbeck Marble', *Hatcher Review*, V, No.45 (Spring 1998), 48–54

B. Hounsell, 'Portland and its Stone', *Mine & Quarry Engineering* (April 1952), 107–114

R. Legg, 'Cowleaze & the Cliff Quarries', *Dorset County Magazine*, 12 (1970), 12–17

D. Lewer (ed.), *John Mowlem's Swanage* (Wincanton, 1990)

J.E. Mallory, 'Places and Products. VIII. Portland Stone', *Geographical Magazine*, IX, No.5 (Sept 1939), 327–338

J. Phillips, 'Quarr Houses on the Isle of Purbeck, Dorset', *Mining History: Bulletin Peak District Mines Historical Society*, 13, No.2 (1996), 155–162

R.J. Saville, *Langton's Stone Quarries* (Langton Matravers, 1976)

J. Smeaton, *A Narrative of the Building of the Eddystone Lighthouse* (1791)

South Western Stone Co., *Portland Stone* (1933)

P. Stanier, *Stone Quarry Landscapes* (Stroud, 2000)

P. Stanier, *Quarries of England & Wales* (Truro, 1995)

P. Stanier, 'The Quarried Face: evidence from Dorset's cliffstone quarries', *Mining History: Bulletin Peak District Mines Historical Society*, 13, No.2 (1996), 1–9

J. Thomas, *Discover Dorset: Stone Quarrying* (Wimborne, 1998)

P. Trim, *The Quarrying of Portland Stone* (Portland, 1991)

A.M. Wallis, 'The Portland Stone Quarries', *PDNHAS*, 12 (1891), 187–194

W. White, *A Londoner's Walk to the Land's End* (1855)

Potters' Clay

R.G. Bartelot, 'Purbeck Clay', *SDNQ*, XXII, pt CXC (1936), 67–8

Board of Trade, *Report of the Enquiry into the Ball Clay Industry* (1946)

H.S.L. Dewar, 'Josiah Wedgwood and his Dorset Clay', *SDNQ*, XXVII, pt CCLXXII (1960), 275–277

W.K.J. Davies, *Pike Bros, Fayle & Co. Ltd, Furzebrook* (1957)

Pike & Fayle Ltd, *Clay Mines of Dorset, Worked by Pike Bros and Fayle & Co. Ltd of Wareham 1760–1960* (1960)

R. Legg, 'Down the Mine', *Dorset County Magazine*, 31 (1973), 27–33

C.E. Robinson, *A Royal Warren or Picturesque Rambles in the Isle of Purbeck* (1882)

L.T.C. Rolt, *The Potters Field* (Newton Abbot, 1974)

Shale and other Fuels

B. Green, *Kimmeridge Shale, its origins, history and uses* (1886)

R. Legg, *Guide to Purbeck Coast and Shipwreck* (Milborne Port, 1984), 19–31

J.C. Mansel-Pleydell, 'Kimmeridge Shale', *PDNHAFC*, XV (1894), 172–183

Sir A. Strahan, *Mem. Geol. Survey Special Reports on the Mineral Resources of GB, Vol. VII. Mineral Oil, Kimmeridge Oil-Shale, Lignites, Jets, Cannel Coals, Natural Gas, England & Wales* (2nd ed., 1920)

H. Torrens, 'The Coal Seekers', *Dorset County Magazine*, 44 (1975), 31–9

Ironstone Working

L. Popplewell, *Ironstone Canyon; The Hengistbury Head Mining Company* (Bournemouth, 1986)

J. Thomas, 'The Building Stones of Dorset: Part 3. Inferior Oolite, Forest Marble, Cornbrash and Corallian Limestones', *PDNHAS*, 116 (1994), 63.

Lime Burning

D. Pushman, *Swanworth* (Langton Matravers, 1995)

P. Stanier, 'Dorset Limekilns: a first survey', *PDNHAS*, 115 (1993), 33–49

P. Stanier, 'More Dorset Limekilns', *PDNHAS*, 117 (1995), 91–94

Cement Manufacturing

J. Draper, 'Quarrying the Lias at Lyme', *PDNHAS*, 123 (2001), 15–22

Brick Making

M. Hammond, *Bricks and Brickmaking* (Princes Risborough, 1981)

M.D.P. Hammond, 'Brick Kilns: An Illustrated Survey', *Inds. Arch. Rev.*, I, No.2 (1977), 171–192

M.S. Ross, 'Long Cross Brickworks, Shaston (Shaftesbury) St James, Dorset', *PDNHAS*, 112 (1990), 146–9

M.S. Ross, 'Brickmaking at Gillingham and Motcombe, Dorset', *PDNHAS*, 113 (1991), 17–22

D. Young, 'Brickmaking at Broadmayne', *PDNHAS*, 89 (1968), 318–324

D. Young, 'Brickmaking in Dorset', *PDNHAS*, 93 (1971), 213–242

D. Young, 'Brickmaking at Weymouth, Dorset', *Industrial Archaeology*, 9 (1972), 188–96

Tiles, Pipes and Pots

D. Algar, A. Light & P. Copland-Griffiths, *The Verwood and District Potteries: A Dorset Industry* (Ringwood, 1979; 2nd ed., 1987)

Anon, *Poole Pottery: The First 100 Years of the Story of Poole Pottery, 1873–1973* (Poole, 1973)

A.J.A. Cooksey, 'Jenning's South Western Pottery, Parkstone', *Industrial Archaeology*, 6 (1969), 164–71

A.J. Cooksey, 'Tobacco-Pipe makers of Poole', *SDNQ*, XXX, No.229 (1974), 28–30.

P. Copland-Griffiths, *Discover Dorset: Potteries* (Wimborne, 1998)

P. Copland-Griffiths & C. Butterworth, 'Excavations of the 17th century kiln at Horton, Dorset', *PDNHAS*, 112 (1990), 23–32

J. Hawkins, *The Poole Potteries* (1980)

L. Hayward (ed. by P. Atterbury), *Poole Pottery – Carter & Company and their Successors 1873–1998* (Shepton Beauchamp, 1998)

L. Myers, *1873–1973: The First 100 Years of the story of Poole Pottery* (1973)

D. Young, 'The Architectural Pottery', *PDNHAS*, 92 (1970), 212–213

D. Young, 'The Verwood Potteries', *PDNHAS*, 101 (1979), 103–120

Corn Milling

J. Addison & R. Wailes, 'Dorset Watermills', *Trans. Newcomen Soc.*, XXXV (1962–63), 193–216

J. Addison & R. Wailes, 'Addendum to Dorset Watermills', *Trans. Newcomen Soc.*, XXXVI (1963–64), 175–181

J. Addison, 'Second Addendum to Dorset Watermills', *Trans. Newcomen Soc.*, XLI (1968–69), 139–162

M. Bone, 'Dorset Windmills', *SDNQ*, XXXIII (1995), 360–363

H.S.L. Dewar, 'The Windmills, Watermills and Horsemills of Dorset', *PDNHAS*, 82 (1960), 109–132

M. Papworth, M. Watts, et al, 'Watermills on the Kingston Lacy Estate, Dorset', *Inds. Arch. Review*, XVIII, No.1 (1995), 106–116

P. Stanier, *Discover Dorset: Mills* (Wimborne, 2000)

M. Watts, *Water and Wind Power* (Princes Risborough, 2000)

Beer

A. Barnard, *Noted Breweries of Britain & Ireland* (1891)

B.G. Cox, 'Ansty Brewery', *Dorset Year Book* (1970/71), 49–53

H. Janes, *Hall & Woodhouse 1777–1977: independent family brewers* (1977)

J. Seekings, *Thomas Hardy's Brewer: the story of Eldridge Pope & Co.* (Wimborne, 1988)

J. Young, *Old Dorset Brewers* (Exeter, 1986)

Malt

A. Patrick, Establishing a Typology for the Buildings of the Floor Malting Industry, *Inds. Arch. Rev., XVIII, No.2 (1996), 180–200*

Hemp and Flax Industries

A. Sanctuary, *Rope, Twine and Net Making* (Princes Risborough, 1980)

M. Bone, 'Bridport Textile Industry 1814–1945', *SDNQ*, XXXI (1981), 141–154

M. Bone, 'The Bridport Flax and Hemp Industry', *Bristol Industrial Archaeology Society Journal*, 18 (1986), 19–31

J. Pahl, 'The Rope and Net Industry of Bridport: Some Aspects of its History and Geography', *PDNHAS*, 82 (1960), 143–154

P.P. Roberts, 'Richard Roberts, flax spinner', *PDNHAS*, 99 (1977), 11–18

E.B. Short, 'Bridport textile industry', *SDNQ*, XXXI, pt 315 (1982), 205–9

Woollen and Silk Textiles

E.O. Cockburn, *Sherborne Silk Mills and Marglass* (Sherborne, 1984; 2nd ed. 1991)
H. Symonds, 'The Silk Industry in Wessex', *PDNHAS*, 37 (1916), 66–93
C.H. Mayo, 'Gillingham Silk Industry', *SDNQ*, XIV (1915), 289–92

Founders and Engineers

E. Course, 'Engineering in Rural Areas', *Inds. Arch. Rev.*, XVIII, No.2 (1996), 151–64
R. Wear & E. Lees, *Stephen Lewin and the Poole Foundry* (1978)
R.A. Whitehead, *A century of service: an illustrated history of Eddison Plant Hire Limited* (1968)

Food Processing and Paper Making

A.H. Shorter, 'Paper-mills in Dorset', *SDNQ*, XXV, No.239 (1948), 144–148
B. Flint, *Wimborne Minster 1700–1900: The Paper Makers* (Wimborne, 1984)

Moving Times: Roads

R.C. Anderson, *The History of the Tramways of Bournemouth and Poole* (1964)
L. Chubb, et al, *Dorset Toll-House Survey* (Dorchester, 1977)
M. de G. Eedle, *Horn Hill Tunnel* (Beaminster, 1994)
D. Gerhold, A Dorset Carrier in 1830, *PDNHAS*, 115 (1993), 29–32
R. Good, *The Old Roads of Dorset* (1966)
W.G. Gow, *Dorset Milestone Survey* (Dorchester, 1980)
D. McFetrich & J. Parsons, *Discover Dorset: Bridges* (Wimborne, 1998)
A.J. Miller, *Poole Turnpike Trust 1756–1882* (Poole, 1977)
W.P. Ransom, *Bournemouth Transport, Parts 1 & 2* (Bournemouth, 1982)
D. Viner, 'The Toll-House at Charminster', *PDNHAS*, 92 (1970), 155
D. Viner, 'The Wimborne and Puddletown Turnpike Trust (1847) and the toll-house at Athelhampton', *PDNHAS*, 104 (1982), 25–32
B. Wallage, 'The traction engines of Portland', *Dorset Year Book* (1996), 71–4
A.J. Wallis, *Dorset Bridges, A History and Guide* (1974)

Railways and Tramways

J.G. Fraser, 'Description of the Lydgate and of the Buckhorn Weston Railway Tunnels', *Min. Proc. Inst. Civil Engineers*, XXII (1862–63), 371–84
M. Hawkins, *The Somerset & Dorset, Then & Now* (Wellingborough, 1986)
B.L. Jackson, *The Abbotsbury Branch* (Didcot, 1989)
B.L. Jackson, *Isle of Portland Railways, vol. 1. The Admiralty and Quarry Railways* (Usk, 1999)
B.L. Jackson, *Isle of Portland Railways, vols. 2–3* (Usk, 2000)
R.W. Kidner, *The Railways of Purbeck* (Usk, 3rd ed. 2000)
G. Lanning, 'The Wool-Bovington Railway', *SDNQ*, XXXII (1988), 679–82
J.H. Lucking, *Dorset's Railways* (Wimborne, 1982)
C.G. Maggs, *Branch Lines of Dorset* (Stroud, 1996)
M.J. Messenger, 'The Portesham Tramway', *Industrial Railway Record*, 101 (1985), 280–81
V. Mitchell & K. Smith, *Branch Line to Lyme Regis*, (Midhurst, 1987)
V. Mitchell & K. Smith, *Branch Lines around Wimborne*, (Midhurst, 1992)
M. Oakley, *Discover Dorset: Railway Stations* (Wimborne, 2001)
L. Oppitz, *Lost Railways of Dorset* (Newbury, 2001)
L. Popplewell, 'The Narrow Gauge Clay Railways of Purbeck', *Dorset Year Book* (1978), 93–100
W.F. Simms, *Railways of Kimmeridge* (Rustington, 1999)

Ports and Shipping

R. Clammer, *Cosens of Weymouth 1918 to 1996* (Truro, 2001)

A.E. Cocksedge, *Bridport harbour: ships built 1769–1879* (Bridport, 1992)

G.J. Davies, 'Poole shipping in the eighteenth century', *PDNHAS*, 116 (1994), 21–25

G.W. Hannah, 'The evolution of Bridport harbour', *PDNHAS*, 108 (1986), 27–31

J.H. Lucking, *The Great Western at Weymouth: a railway and shipping history* (Newton Abbot, 1971)

J.H. Lucking, *The Weymouth Harbour Tramway* (Poole, 1986)

H.G. Male, *Exported Wealth: The Story of Stone by Sea* (Portland, 1995)

P.J. Perry, 'Bridport Harbour and the Hemp and Flax Trade, 1815–1914', *PDNHAS*, 86 (1964), 231–34

The Water Supply Industry

J. Cooper, 'Sutton Poyntz Pumping Station', *International Stationary Steam Engine Society Bulletin*, 22, No.3 (2000), 37–43

G.M. Dear, *From watermill to waterworks at Christchurch* (Bournemouth, 1978)

F. Howarth & J.A. Young, *A Brief History of the Water Supply of Shaftesbury, Dorset* (Shaftesbury, 1972)

J. Nash, 'Castleton's Waterwheel', *Dorset Life* (June 1989), 51–53

R. Pountain, *Castleton Pumping Station, Sherborne: A History* (Sherborne, 2001)

M.S. Ross, 'The Water Supply of Kington Magna', *PDNHAS*, 115 (1993), 173–74

W. Whitaker & W. Edwards, *Wells and Springs of Dorset* (1926)

Housing and Recreation

C. Church & E. Course, 'The Industrial Archaeology of a Seaside Resort', *Southampton University Inds. Arch. Group Jnl*, 5 (1996), 4–8

E.O. Cockburn, 'The Cerne Abbas Union Workhouse', *PDNHAS*, 94 (1973), 89–94

S.R. Lough, et al, *Dorset Workhouses* (Dorchester, 1980)

D.M.H. Reeby, 'Weymouth's Spas – Nottington and Radipole', *PDNHAS*, 116 (1994), 33–44

Military Matters

M. Boddy & J. West, 'Imperial Works and Worthy Kings – the Building of Portland Breakwater', *Dorset Year Book* (1981), 39–43

M. Boddy & J. West, 'The Portland breakwaters: a Victorian achievement', *Industrial Archaeology*, 16 (1981), 238–54

M.R. Bowditch, *Cordite – Poole: A Short Account of the Royal Navy Cordite Factory* (Stroud, 1983)

M.R. Bowditch, & L. Hayward, *A Pictorial Record of the Royal Naval Cordite Factory, Holton Heath* (Wool, 1996)

I. Brown, et al, *20th Century Defences in Britain: An Introductory Guide* (York, 1995)

G. Carter, *The Royal Navy at Portland since 1845* (Liskeard, 1987)

T.P. Hattersley, 'Portland Breakwater', *Dorset County Magazine*, 27 (1972), 48–56

G. Lamming, 'The RAF Station at Ringstead', *SDNQ*, XXXII, pt 330 (1989), 795–796

A. Saunders, *Channel Defences* (1997)

E.M. Wallace, 'Developing Radar in Dorset', *Dorset Year Book* (1991), 38–45

Some of the books and papers in this short list cover more than one industry, although they are only named once, and most will give further sources of information. In addition, maps, guide books, trade directories (*Kelly's, Harrod's, Pigot's*, etc) and newspapers such as the *Dorset County Chronicle*, all create a useful picture of industrial activity. Periodicals with occasional references to industries include the *Dorset County Magazine, Dorset Year Book, Somerset & Dorset Notes & Quarries (SDNQ)* and the *Proceedings of the Dorset Natural History & Archaeological Society (PDNHAS)*. All these and more can be consulted at the Dorset County Reference Library in Dorchester.

Primary sources are to be found in the archives of the Dorset County Record Office. Documents, ledgers and papers, although not always complete, cover a variety of industries such as railways, turnpike roads, quarries, lime burning, mills, flax, silk and a host of miscellaneous industries. Early maps which can be useful for industries include Isaac Taylor's map of 1765, the Tithe Apportionment maps of around 1840 and many estate maps and plans of all periods.

❧ INDEX ❧